A brief 'I spy' guide to places associa[...]
past and present in [...]
and a contemporary photographic record of [...]
fishing boats kept in these places.

The Fishing Boats & Ports
of
CORNWALL
An Alternative Way to Explore Cornwall
by
Stewart Lenton
(With contributions by Liz Lenton)

Channel View Publishing
Plymouth
Channel View, Andurn Estate,
Down Thomas
PLYMOUTH PL9 0AT

First Published in 2006
Revised 2013
By Channel View Publishing Plymouth
Channel View, Andurn Estate, Down Thomas,
Plymouth PL9 0AT
slenton@btinternet.com   www.fishportboats.co.uk

ISBN 978-0-9554023-7-1
The Fishing Boats & Ports of Cornwall Second Edition

Photographs on the Front Cover:-
Above - FH324 Silver Queen, FY91 Manx Ranger, FY869 Mystique II, PZ101 Louise N
Below——Boat Cove, Mousehole, FH740 Rebecca Too, PW28 Our Zoe
Below - **Photographs on the Back Cover:-**
Left to right and top to bottom
Polperro Harbour, PZ699 Boy Matt, PZ336 Nazarene, E519 Rene, FH706 Victoria Ann
FH693 Lizy, Cadgwith Beach, PW41 Black Pearl & PW44 Ellen Mary at Bude

*Every effort has been made to get the information and details of boats correct at the time of
writing . However boats are continually moving around and sometimes spend different times
of year in different ports which might account for some discrepancies. Much information has
been obtained by detective work . If any errors are spotted I apologise, and would be very
grateful for any information to correct it for future versions of the book.   Please contact me
via e-mail at slenton@btinternet.com or through
Channel View Publishing Plymouth
Channel View
Andurn Estate, Down Thomas
Plymouth , PL9 0AT*

Foreword by David Linkie
of Fishing News

For centuries fishing from the numerous coves and harbours located along the approximately 300miles of rugged and remote Cornish coastline has been an integral part of the social fabric of Cornwall.

The hostile but also highly productive North Atlantic waters that surround Cornwall are home to a rich diversity of prime seafood. Including bass, brown crab, dover sole, hake, halibut, lobster, mackerel, monkfish, pilchards, scallops, spider crab and turbot, these valuable species are a familiar sight to local residents and tourists alike.

Whereas in years gone by, fresh Cornish seafood would be eaten in close proximity to where it was caught and brought ashore, this situation is considerably different today. Regardless of species, a large proportion of seafood landed in Cornwall today is highly valued throughout Europe in such countries as France, Italy and Spain.

Further evidence of the renowned reputation fishermen in Cornwall have for delivering top quality seafood is that their catches are much sought after and highly valued by well-known chefs and leading restaurants in London, as well as throughout south-west England.

While the main fishing methods such as gill-netting, hand-lining, potting and trawling are the same in principle today as they were several generations ago, considerable changes can be seen in the catch storage methods used by modern fishermen.

Larger vessels are equipped with hi-tech ice machines and refrigerated fishrooms to ensure that catches are stored in optimum condition, while small single-handed cove boats carry insulated containers into which fish are immediately placed. Little wonder then that Cornish seafood is held in such high regard!

One of the main characteristics of fishing in Cornwall is the level of natural diversity spanning both the size and type of vessel and their place of operation.

By including every location from where fishing vessels operate daily in Cornwall, 'The Fishing Boats and Ports of Cornwall' provides a comprehensive and invaluable insight into a way of life that continues to fascinate people from all backgrounds.

Perhaps to a casual observer, fishing is underpinned by continuity and stability. Whilst this is largely true when viewed from the perspective of annual catches and their composition, the same cannot always be said about the vessels of the Cornish fishing fleet.

To progress their individual businesses and ensure they are in line with fishing opportunities and marketing requirements, skippers/owners regularly buy and sell their boats. This well established pattern leads to continual changes in the vessels fishing from each location. Having purchased another vessel, a skipper then often renames it in line with a long-established family tradition.

In order to ensure coverage of these changes, as well as to provide up-to-date photographs, author Stewart Lenton has spent countless hours visiting every harbour in Cornwall in order to provide highly detailed and first-hand coverage of the Cornish fishing fleet.

In years to come, 'The Fishing Boats and Ports of Cornwall' will provide a valuable historical record of what for many families continues to be a traditional way of life, and one that is therefore of continuing importance throughout Cornwall.

PORTS

After the introduction **details of the Cornish ports follow in clockwise order round the coast**, starting at the River Tamar on the Cornish side of Plymouth Sound, finishing at Bude on the Cornwall/Devon border on the North Coast.

Each Port is identified on the map inside the front cover by a number in red which also appears on the left hand side of the coloured title bar for the corresponding Port description.

The Contents index on page v gives the page number where each port section begins.

On the section for each Port there are;-

a. **Some brief details about the port**, and where applicable notes on other landing places in the area, and photographs of the port.

b. **A list of boats** known to be operating, or have operated since 2006, from that port in alpha-numerical order of registration (see below)

c. **Photographs of each boat** in the same numerical order as the list of boats in that port. Below each photograph is the date on which it was taken.

BOATS

The list of boats (b. above) operating from each port indicates -

Type of fishing, Length overall in metres, Engine Kilowatt power, Year and country of manufacture. In the column for hull construction,

S=Steel, W=Wood, and F=Fibreglass, A=Aluminium

A 'p' against the boat's name indicates that there is a photograph of that boat.

(*No ' p' means that a photograph has not been taken either because the boat has moved from the area, or just not been seen!*)

At the end of the book is included:

Two lists of all the boats known to be operating from Cornwall including the Isles of Scilly.

The first list is in alpha-numerical order of registration. This list only includes those vessels that were actually registered at the time of publication

The second list is an alphabetical list by name of all the Cornwall boats that were either present around the Cornish coast or have been seen at the Cornish ports since the publication of the first edition of the 'Fishing Boats & Ports of Cornwall' in 2006.

To find the photograph of a particular boat

1. Look up either the name in the alphabetical list, or the number in the alpha-numerical list.
2. Note the home port of the boat,
3. Then consult the relevant port pages *(for page number see contents index on page v)* and look up the boat in the photographs of boats in that port which are in order of registration number. *(See c. above)*

No list will ever be completely up to date since there is a continual state of change, as boats get bought and sold, new vessels arrive on the scene, and older vessels are either de-registered, scrapped, or left to die gracefully. Boats can also change appearance as they get repainted in different colour schemes, or even undergo more dramatic modifications, such as a change in position of the wheelhouse as illustrated by the photographs in the section of the Introduction beginning at pages ix.

Boat Spotting - It is suggested that as you visit the ports and coast and personally find each boat, you can indicate this by ticking the 'p' column in pencil, or keeping a separate list of boats seen with the date they were seen inside the back cover.

Contents

INTRODUCTION

No Cornish location is far from the sea which is possibly why it is such a favoured holiday destination. There are sandy beaches and those renowned for good surf, cliff top walks with outstanding views, and impressive rugged rock formations upon which ferocious tides may crash and bellow their fury. Such are some of the seaside delights that attract people to visit and revisit to this part of the world in all seasons; whether they be artists drawn by the quality of the light for which the far West Cornwall is celebrated, or whether they come to follow the many active coastal pursuits, or

Wild Flowers on coast at Mousehole

Fishing Boat returning to Cadgwith Cove

perhaps just to wander, watch and dream. Who does not enjoy visiting the many attractive little Cornish coves and harbours? The fishing boats found in them still make colourful additions to scenes that are capable of firing the imagination with romantic images of the past; of smuggler's haunts, old Cornish Luggers, and the like - such imaginations possibly first kindled by other lovers of Cornwall who have used it as a setting for their artistic or literary works. The region today is a far cry from what it was in the past, when huge numbers of people would be found engaging in one of the many aspects of the fishing industry. Some of the traditions and historic background to that industry are outlined later *(see pages xxviii-xxix)*. Today's visitors still find fascination in seeking out the remains of these old occupations. But how many people enjoying the pretty harbours and coves give much thought to the lives of those who work their present day fishing boats? The TV programs like 'The Fisherman's Apprentice' that was filmed in Cadgwith in 2011 *(see page 74)*, and broadcast in 2012, about life as a member of its small fishing fleet, and the 2006 BBC documentary 'Trawlermen', could prompt some people to think about the problems faced by those who bring back the fish we eat. 'Trawlermen' featured the working lives and

Evidence of Old Fishing Industry

conditions of the crews of several trawlers operating out of Peterhead in Scotland. Although the subtitles, that were at times used to translate broad Scottish accents to the 'Sassenachs' caused some offence up north - the visual impact of the trawlermen's working conditions needed no explanation. We saw sleep starved men, on slippery decks handling difficult equipment buffeted by strong seas or relentlessly gutting fish over long hours in wet, icy conditions. We felt the anticipation of nets being hauled in, often to find that they contained precious few fish, and possibly some that they did not want to catch. Sometimes nets might contain large boulders, putting strain on valuable fishing gear *(see page xvi)* and often causing extensive damage. Viewers must have been impressed by the skill, experience and instinct of skippers who had to make difficult decisions about where to fish to maximise their catch and minimise the fuel expenditure. When these equations were unfavourable there was the possibility of crewmen being laid off, or returning less than a living wage to their long suffering families who had endured days on end with no man in the home. Some factors are comparable, whatever the size or type of vessel and wherever she is worked. Because the ferocity of the sea can be as unpredictable and treacherous as ever, today's fishermen experience the same dangers faced by their grandfathers, despite the availability of more sophisticated equipment. In the seven years since this book was first published the Devon & Cornwall fishing fraternity has to date known eleven serious incidents involving the loss of fishing boats with three fatalities *(see pages ix & x)*. They include the tragic death of a popular Looe fisherman who died when fishing alone after his protective clothing got caught in deck machinery. His MP widow, Sheryll Murray has proved to be a useful voice in Parliament for Cornish fishermen.

Aside from the often dangerous working conditions, how many visitors to Cornwall understand the deep concerns that those employed in commercial fishing and its related occupations now have about their work? Perhaps they have heard '*fishing quotas*' mentioned in the news media in connection with a recent campaign by certain celebrities to raise public awareness of the scandalous EU regulation that stipulates that any fish accidentally caught by a boat outside its 'quota' must be returned to the sea and not landed even if it is already dead! They may also have heard concerns expressed by conservationists' about overfishing and damage to the sea bed by certain types of fishing. Fishing today, if it ever was, is not just a matter of putting to sea and catching as many fish as possible, like the harvesting of the shoals of pilchards when they were sighted off the Cornish coast in days of old. It is a highly regulated and often controversial business. Perhaps this is inevitable given the

sophisticated and efficient equipment to seek out and extract fish available to some large modern fishing vessels. There appears to be a perceived divergence between the interests of 'Conservationists' who are concerned about natural resources, and the fishermen who might appear to be depleting or damaging them. But this is to over simplify the issues. Depletion of fish stocks is something that no fisherman wants, because their very existence depends on a plentiful supply of fish, and conservation ideas are not new to them. What is new, since the advent of the European Union (EU) with its 1973 Common Fisheries Policy (CFP), is having fishing policies decided by those not directly involved in fishing, and often far removed from the fishing grounds concerned. The CFP was set up to regulate fishing activity by its member states in order to share common marine resources and conserve fish stocks. This it does by annually setting 'quotas' for each member state from the Total Allowable Catch (TAC). This is the maximum allowable catch overall for each species in the period, fixed annually by the EU Council of Ministers on advice from the International Council for Exploration of the Sea (ICES). The ICES promotes and coordinates work by a huge number of scientists doing all manner of marine research by which it is able to monitor and advise on the situation in the North Atlantic. The EU also has its own scientific advisers, the Scientific, Technical and Economic Committee of Fisheries (STECF), and they advise the EU taking into account the work of the ICES. The TAC, having been decided, must then be apportioned to member states to arrive at each state's national quota. There is obvious difficulty in balancing the needs of each member state, particularly for those that have large areas traditionally associated with certain fisheries, especially if they are highly dependent on fishing with little else to boost their economy. Restrictions may also be placed by the EU Council of Ministers on the allowable number of fishing days at sea, and there has been a tendency for an automatic percentage reduction to both quota and fishing days to be applied annually. It is the responsibility of the member state concerned to divide its national quota between its various fishing grounds, and to police and enforce adherence to quota in them. There are several countries engaged in fishing the same areas of sea, and the decisions on how the TAC is allocated, to arrive at each country's quota, have been made annually in difficult 'horse trading' type meetings of ministers who are responsible for fishing from the countries who have chosen to be bound by the CFP of the EU. (Writing in 2013, the major fishing countries of Iceland, Norway, Greenland and the Faroe Islands are not members with potential for obvious problems and Iceland and the Faroes were causing concern by overfishing massive amounts of mackerel)

As indicated above, quotas are specific for each type of fish, but there is a limit to what can be done in the way of modifying nets to allow non target fish to escape. Inevitably there will quite frequently be times when the wrong species is accidentally caught, and by the time the catch is sorted on board, the fish are usually dead. This '*Bycatch*' is unavoidable but it cannot be landed, and therefore has to be returned to the sea as '*discards*' even though such fish are no longer viable! This practice benefits nobody, and it is hard to defend in terms of world resources, but to do it in the name of preservation of fish stocks is unbelievable! It is not hard to imagine what having to throw perfectly edible dead fish overboard does to a fisherman's morale! In Feb 2013 there came some hope that this abhorrent practice may soon just form a shocking page in history with the news that the European parliament had voted for sweeping reforms of the controversial CFP. The package included measures to protect endangered stocks and end discards. (All 'bycatch' will be landed and logged in future instead of estimates given so that this can be included in calculations). It was thought it could become law by 2014, but there needed to be more talks with the 27 EU governments. Under the new proposals, the EU would shift from the current bargaining over quotas to fishing based on 'Maximum Sustainable Yield (MSY)' (taking from a fish stock that amount which can continually be replaced by reproduction allowing for natural death). The phasing in of MSY depends on collecting more scientific data about the rate at which different marine species reproduce. These new proposals will need much working out. With the number of states involved, and the necessary collection and interpretation of data it would seem unlikely to happen very quickly but the ICES has already done much work towards it. Fishermen and scientists have increasingly been cooperating in gathering facts. Fishermen have much traditional and local knowledge and the scientists' modern equipment allows more precise measurements of recovery in overfished stocks. Fishermen are also using electronic logbooks to meticulously record catches and a Yorkshire trawlerman even volunteered to have CCTV on board to monitor catch and discards. All must be important in calculating MSY. How the MSY would work for fisheries remains to be seen. MEP's have been talking about a need to help fishermen through a transitional period as fishing capacity shrinks to allow stocks to recover. A fishing alliance, *'Europeche'*, says *'the reforms are too sudden and too radical'*. There is certainly much for fishermen to 'get their heads round'!

In Cornwall, fishermen are not only bound by EU policies, but also additional UK regulations and even local Cornish bye-laws. The latter concern things like area specific permits to fish for lobster, crabs, and crayfish for profit, and submitting monthly returns on catches, regulation minimum sizes allowed to be taken, the correct measuring devices, and types of nets that may be legally carried on board etc. These were administered by the old Cornwall Sea Fisheries Committee (CSFC) but as a result of the Marine and Coastal Access Act of 2009 the Cornwall Inshore Fisheries and Conservation Authority (CIFCA) was established in 2011 and it has taken over this role as well the enforcing of some national and European fisheries legislation. The IFCA however has a much broader remit for the sustainable management of the offshore marine environment. It aims to work closely with fishermen in exchanging ideas, and has been meeting with different fisherman groups at regular intervals. All bye-laws are being reviewed to ensure that they are relevant to the present situation. It performs research surveys, for example, the recent monitoring of shellfish stocks within estuaries, eg; cockles in the Camel Estuary. The CIFCA can impart important information on the breeding and movement patterns of various species. An interesting example is the fact that sea bass have benefitted from the trend to warmer UK winters. Young bass have thrived and they are now breeding much further north in Britain. Surveys of juvenile bass have recently been undertaken in the Fal and Helford rivers. In carrying out its tasks the CIFCA operates 4 vessels,- a 27m patrol boat 'Saint Piran' *(See picture Page 93)* which acts as a mother vessel to 'Lyonesse' - a 6.5 metre Rigid Inflatable Boat (RIB), a standalone 6.5m RIB 'Avalon', and a 7m multi-hulled survey/research boat 'Kerwyn'.

Another potential cause for concern to our Cornish fishermen comes from the rush to establish renewable energy sources offshore. There is a limit to the numbers of solar panels and wind generators that can be accommodated on land and apparently a vast ocean around us with obvious power in its movements. The employment potential and boost to local economy gained by offshore generator construction would be welcome. However the presence of such generators provides not only a physical obstacle to boats, but potential to change fish behaviour in ways that effect fishing. All offshore structures cause degrees of disturbance to the sea bed, surrounding water and air, during their construction, operation and decommissioning phases, with the potential to disrupt the balance of marine life right along the food chain. Sound and 'shock wave' effects of pile driving can be traumatic. The generating devices produce sound, and electromagnetic forces are emitted from cables. The consequences might mean fish being displaced from spawning or fishing grounds, inhibiting reproduction and survival with resultant reduced catches. Scientists have been measuring effects in different marine species but it is a huge and complicated task and the need for 'renewables' is urgent. So far in Cornwall the major development has been a wave hub consisting of a giant socket sited on the seabed 10 miles off the North Coast with a large underwater cable connecting to the grid network ashore at Hayle. Wave energy devices are to be 'plugged' in and tested *'on a scale not seen anywhere before'*. The project also aims to develop, build and test a floating offshore wind turbine to investigate whether floating wind farms could play a cost-effective role in helping to meet the UK's energy needs.

One might add that in all the above considerations, unpredictable and often conflicting political agendas come into play at given times. Thus getting things right for everyone is a highly contentious and difficult task.

Liz Lenton

Commercial Fishing in Cornwall

There has been quite a significant change in the type of fishing which is carried out in Cornwall since my first book was published in 2006. This is summarised in the table below.

Changes in Cornwall since 2006.						
Year	Trawler/Scallopers	Netters	Potters	Liners	Other	Total
2006	105	270	139	109	30	653
2013	69	228	127	205	23	651

Compared with many parts of the UK the total numbers of registered vessels has remained remarkably constant with little change. The greatest loss has been in the number of trawlers operating and this has been particularly noticeable in Newlyn, where many of the older less fuel efficient beam trawlers have been retired *(see page 87)*. The significant drop in trawler numbers, and to a lesser extent the drop in the number of boats engaged in potting and netting has been more than compensated for by the increase in the number of boats used for line fishing which has almost doubled. Some of these have moved round from St Ives where there has been a drop in numbers from 52 to 29. Needless to say the total tonnage and size of boats in Newlyn has reduced considerably as a beam trawler is many times the size of a small liner. The number of boats in Newlyn over 20m in length has more than halved from 55 to 23 and the number of boats over 10m dropped from 66 to 45. Away from Newlyn many ports have remained almost unchanged, while others have seen considerable changes such as at Looe, Mevagissey and Padstow where a large number of the boats have been replaced by newer vessels. Generally the type of fishing has remained fairly constant but Looe has reduced the number of trawlers with several of them moving to Plymouth where the tide is less restrictive. The numbers of boats in Looe over 10m has dropped from 19 to only 8 while Newquay and Padstow combined have seen an increase from 6 to 11. It is important to note that the numbers in the table above are those boats that are registered, while the numbers of boats actively fishing is almost certainly less. They also include many boats that are owned by part time fishermen who may be fishing less than one day a week, and possibly only in the summer months.

Many of the vessels used for line fishing are about 5-6 metres in length and called 'Toshers'. They are open, but very seaworthy boats used for both netting and either hand or rod lining, fishing for pilchards, cod, mackerel and eels. Most of them operate in the areas round The Lizard and Lands End. On the Isles of Scilly, and sometimes elsewhere in Cornwall, these boats are called 'punts', although they bear no resemblance to punts as generally known. Netters over 10 metres length are restricted by law from fishing close inshore to preserve fish stocks, but this restriction does not apply to the smaller boats, and many of the 'Toshers' are able to take advantage of this by netting and hand, or long line, fishing inshore. The advantage of both line fishing and ring netting (see later) is that the fish are landed relatively undamaged, compared with the gill damage that occurs using nets, and this makes the fish more presentable for the dinner table, a feature which is much desired on the continent to which many of the fish so caught are destined.

Fishing remains as one of the most dangerous occupations in the UK and in the 7 years since 2006 ten fishing vessels based in the South West have been lost.

Details are as follows:- At 0600 on 3rd October 2007, the Helford based boat 'Lady Patricia of Helford' (FH214) sank at the mouth of the Helford River after colliding with 'Blythe Spirit' (FH683) from Falmouth in fog. A few days later she was recovered, and was back in service by mid March the following year. The 'Blythe Spirit' was able to make her way back to Falmouth, but was too badly damaged for repair and was scrapped.

On 28th May 2008, the Newlyn Netter 'Girl Patricia' (PZ57) sank 30 miles west of the Isles of Scilly. The crew were all rescued.

On 23rd August 2008, the 'Levan-Mor of Looe' (FY269) sank 20 miles south of Penzance when the trawl got caught on the seabed. The recently developed 'Man Overboard Device' triggered overdue action and the crewman was rescued.

**Memorial to Fisherman
Ben Cochrane in St Mawes**

*Inscription reads -
"A Man who loved the Sea as
much as we all loved him"*

On 12th March 2011, the Newlyn based netter 'Ben My Chree' (PZ645) sank 15 miles NE of the Isles of Scilly and the crew were rescued by the Scilly lifeboat and the RN Culdrose rescue helicopter.

On 11th April 2011, the Looe based 'Norvik' (FY44) hit rocks and sank off Polperro and the crewman was rescued by other nearby fishing boats.

On 20th December 2011 the Mevagissey converted ring netter 'Heather Anne' (FY126) capsized and sank after making a huge catch of sprats off Dodman Point. Even after offloading much of her catch onto two other boats she had 10.5 tons of catch on board reducing her freeboard, as a result of which she subsequently capsized. The skipper was rescued by the fishing vessel 'Lauren Kate' but his crewman went down with the boat. The boat was later recovered and was seen on the quayside at Falmouth docks and later at Mylor shipyard for repair. *(See pictures below)*

Ring Netter 'Heather Anne' (FY126)   **On Quayside at Falmouth Docks after recovery**   **Undergoing repairs at Mylor shipyard**

On 11th March 2012 the Millbrook potter 'Arandora Star' (E44) suddenly sank off Bigbury but the crewman managed to get into his life-raft and send up a flare which was seen by a member of the public ashore, and he was rescued by Plymouth lifeboat. Only three weeks earlier she had caught a 100 year old, 32 inch lobster weighing 12.9 lbs in the same area.

On 2nd September 2012, the Newlyn based 'Chloe T' (PZ1186) started taking in water, coupled with power failure, fifteen miles south of Bolt Head. The five man crew took to the life rafts and were recued by the RN Culdrose helicopter. The boat subsequently sank.

On 11th September 2012, the 'Sarah Jayne' (BM249) capsized 2.5 miles south of Berry Head. Two crew were rescued by the Brixham lifeboat but one crewman was drowned.

There was another fatality in April 2011 when the owner skipper of the Looe boat 'Our Boy Andrew' (LT1) got his clothing caught in machinery and he was pulled to his death. The boat was found drifting several miles further down the coast and recovered to Fowey.

On 29th December 2013 the 'JCK' (BM17) sank off Torquay when returning from a successful fishing trip in a SWly gale. Following overdue action the skipper's body was found at sea, and though some flotsam was washed ashore, the boat was never found.

On 15th July 2010, one of the beautifully restored heritage fishing vessels, the Penrhyn based 'Pet' (PZ211) broke from her anchor in rough seas off St Peter Port in Guernsey and was swept onto rocks and is currently in a sad state at Gweek boatyard awaiting repair.

PZ211 'Pet' - Before and after hitting rocks off Guernsey

Administrative Centres   The two Administrative Centres for fishing vessels operating in Cornwall, are at Plymouth and Newlyn. Working clockwise around the coast, Plymouth covers from the River Tamar to Polruan on the River Fowey, while Newlyn covers the Cornish coast from Fowey town round Lands End to Bude, including the Isles of Scilly, and Plymouth covers the North Coast from the Devon border. These Administrative Centres regulate catches and ensure adherence to the safety regulations which apply, increasingly, as the size of boat increases. Skippers of fishing vessels greater than ten metres registered length are required by law to keep a 24 hour log of their catches, generally using electronic logs. These logs are presented to the local fisheries officer wherever the catch is landed, and copies of them are then sent on to the vessel's Administrative Centre. The choice of the vessel's Administrative Centre may just be at the request of an individual owner or skipper, and it is quite possible for a vessel operating in the South West to use a Centre completely outside the area. This applies particularly when some boats visit the area for a particular fishing season from as far away as Scotland. For these reasons, boats, although operating from the same port, may be using different Administrative Centres. Skippers/Owners of fishing vessels less than ten metres registered length, were not obliged by law to keep a record of their catches, but usually did so, although they did not have to submit them to the Administrative Centres. This is why so many boats currently in service were specifically designed to be just under ten metres registered length. The rules keep changing however and many owners of the under 10m boats are finding themselves increasingly restricted by fishing regulations of how much, and what, they can catch. Ten metres is also the size above which even more stringent equipment and safety regulations apply. (15 metres length is the next step up, where even further regulations apply). Because the registered length is measured from the bow of the boat to the stern post (where the rudder is mounted), there are a few boats with an overall length of more than 10m, but which are still registered as vessels of 10m or less. The owners of the smaller boats have difficulty, both financially and physically, in installing the requirements for boats of 10m and under into their smaller hulls. Many of them believe that there is a case for less stringent regulations for vessels of say under 6m length. At the time of writing there is a new proposal for fishing boats under seven metres in length to be limited to a ridiculously low maximum permitted total catch of 300kg per year. The only way around that would be to purchase further licenses probably costing thousands of pounds. Boats which fish for salmon and eels and those which are propelled either by rowing or sailing, have been exempt from many of the regulations. Consequently they are also not subject to the same safety requirements. It may well change in the future and all such vessels may have to be registered. This would almost certainly affect the sail powered boats in the oyster fishery in the Fal Estuary, one of which was actually registered until recently.

Registration Ports   The fascinating history behind the fishing boat registration scheme is covered in my booklet 'What is the Meaning of the Numbers and Letters on Fishing Boats?'(ISBN 9780955402333) Anyone wishing to sell his catch commercially has first to register his boat, after which he can obtain a fishing licence. The Ports of Registration round the coast are those ports which have been centres of fishing activities historically, and were also the Custom House Ports for the area. Some of these places still have boats on their registers even though very little, or even no, fishing activity continues from their port. Truro (TO) is an example where there is no activity at all, but a few boats are still registered there, while Fowey (FY), although having one of the largest registered fleets, only has a handful of boats currently operating from Fowey itself. Any fisherman now wishing to obtain a licence to operate from a particular port will apply to be registered by the Registry of Shipping and Seamen (part of the Maritime Coastguard Agency), based in Cardiff. He will then be issued with a number which will follow the letters of the appropriate (usually the nearest) Registration Port. This is called a PLN (Port Letter Number). The registration letters for the Ports of Registration in both Devon and Cornwall are as below.

E	Exeter	PH	Plymouth	SC	Scilly Isles
TH	Teignmouth	FY	Fowey	SS	St Ives
DH	Dartmouth	TO	Truro	PW	Padstow
BM	Brixham	FH	Falmouth	BD	Bideford
SE	Salcombe	PZ	Penzance	BE	Barnstaple

If they wish to reuse an old number, they have to be able to prove that the old number is no longer in use. The registration letters and numbers are painted on the sides of the hull, at bow and stern, on part of the structure facing upwards, to be visible from the air, and on the lifebelts and life-rafts and other boat equipment. The Port of Registration is not necessarily the port from which the vessel operates, since as a boat gets bought and sold, the licence is often sold with it, and the boat continues under its old registration at the port of the new owner. Many owners prefer to keep a shorter number rather than re-register with a longer number. The cost of re-inscribing the five locations on the hull and superstructure and elsewhere adds to the cost of re-registering, and some also believe it unlucky to change the number! Since devolution of the government of Wales however, some owners of under 10 metre boats found that there were advantages to re-registering which outweighed the above considerations. The devolved territories within the UK have operated their own fisheries rules and the restrictions for under 10m Welsh boats are less stringent than for those registered in England. About fifty four owners of SW boats re-registered their boats at Welsh registration ports to take advantage of this - about twenty were from Cornwall. By some quirk in the rules they were not required to have any other connection with a Welsh port. Many chose some of the lesser known Welsh registration ports so that they could keep their old number and only change the port letters. However a 'Concordat' between the fishing authorities in the four countries forming the United Kingdom was signed in September 2012 and it put a stop to this. This required that all boats be registered in a port of their own 'territory', which meant that all Welsh, Scottish and Northern Ireland registered boats that were permanently based in England, had to be re-registered to an English registration port, and all the owners who had changed to Welsh registrations for the above reasons had to revert

The 3 phases of Registration of the Looe Fishing Boat 'OHIO'

SS689 on 03/11/2004
St Ives registered

SA 1238 on 05/07/2012
Swansea registered

FY123 on 01/04/2013
Fowey registered

back to English registrations with a deadline of 1st October 2012 This also applied to boats that had, years ago, been obtained from other territories but had never obtained English registrations. Any owners who did not comply risked losing their licences. One Fisherman is on record having siad that it would cost him about £10,000 to comply. Some owners reverted to their old PLN if it was still available, while others were able to keep the same number while changing the port letters to those of a local registration port, thus reducing the extent of change to the inscriptions of the new PLN in all the required places. The new port registration was not required to be at that of the nearest registration port. This was apparently so that any boat having the same name as another at the same port could register elsewhere in order to comply with Merchant Shipping legislation that stipulates that no two vessels can be registered with the same name in the same port of registration. About 45 owners in Cornwall alone were affected by this change. Nearly a quarter of the Welsh fishing fleet (some 141 boats) were non Welsh registered boats and they had to change to a Welsh port of registration.

In recent years DEFRA, followed by the MMO, have allowed fishermen to choose in which port they wish to register a new boat, which is often not their nearest registration port. Some owners have opted to use a port which has the registered letters of their own name initials. Perhaps not envisaged by the originators of the scheme!!

All the above reasons give some explanation as to why so many boats, which though permanently based in Cornwall, can be found with the registration letters of ports far from their nearest registration port, but at least they are now all registered in English ports.

In 2009, there was a decommissioning scheme in which owners were encouraged to scrap their boats in exchange for a financial settlement. It was intended to reduce the number of fishing vessels operating, and to encourage the scrapping of older vessels, but although that did happen, some surprisingly new boats were scrapped under the scheme. The boats had to be registered in England and be up to a certain standard to be eligible. One owner with a Scottish registered boat not only had to pay for re-registration, but had also to improve his boat to the required standard just so it could be scrapped!! Many owners subsequently put their money into the purchase of more modern, but smaller boats. Thus the overall number of boats has not greatly changed .

CERTIFICATE OF BRITISH REGISTRY

The Merchant Shipping Act 1995
The Merchant Shipping (Registration of Ships) Regulations 1993, as amended

PARTICULARS OF SHIP

Name Of Ship:

Official Number:	**C17920**	Radio Call Sign
IMO Number / HIN:		Port **PENZANCE**
Type of Ship	**FISHING VESSEL**	Port Letters and numbers:
Engine Make / model:	**BMC 1500**	Engine ID No. **5085**
Total Engine Power:	**16.00** kW	
Overall Length:	**5.87** metres	Registered Length: **5.87** metres
Breadth:	**2.24** metres	Depth: **1.03** metres
Gross Tonnage:	**2.16**	Net Tonnage **2.16**
Year of Build	**1994**	Country of Build **UNITED KINGDOM**
Date of entry into service:	**25/06/2003**	
Type of Registration:	**SIMPLE**	

This Certificate was issued on **7 April**

This Certificate expires on: **24 June**

Signed ....

For and on behalf of the Registrar, General

by the Maritime and Coastguard Agency, an Executive Agency of th

> The all important piece of paper!!

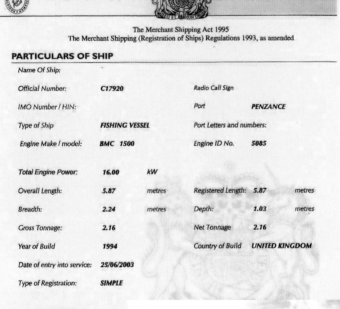

Right - Memorial on Newlyn Seafront to Fishermen 'Lost at Sea'
(Unveiled by HRH Princess Royal on 11th October 2007)

THE TYPES of FISHING VESSELS

The fishing industry, in Devon and Cornwall together, accounts for approximately half the entire fish landings in England, in terms of both quantity and value, and although there has been a gradual decline in the fishing industry generally, the decline has been less marked in the West Country, which is fortunate in having a rich variety of fish in its waters. There are seven main types of fishing vessels. A brief description of each follows.

Multi Purpose Trawlers These trawlers are the mainstay of the inshore fishing fleets and are used mainly to catch demersal fish on the sea bed. The rocky coastline around Cornwall is less suited to inshore trawling and the numbers of such trawlers is less than can be found in Devon, and there has been a significant drop in the trawler numbers in Cornwall recently. The bag-like conical trawl net is streamed on two lines attached to heavy boards which are towed at an angle so that they hold the trawl net open. These boards are called 'Otter Boards'. The top of the net is attached to buoyancy to keep it from the bottom. In port or in transit the otter boards will be seen, usually suspended externally, on the aft ends of the vessels on both sides. Small derricks are usually fitted to handle them and powerful winches are needed to haul in the trawl net. The trawl will be between 1/4

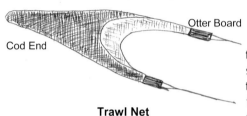

Cod End — Otter Board

Trawl Net

mile and 1 mile in length, depending on the size of vessel, and may be carried out at a variety of depths depending on the target species, and is towed at a speed of 2- 3 knots. When trawling, the boats are very restricted in manoeuvrability, with only small changes in direction possible, since otherwise the otter boards will be pulled close together thus closing the net. When the trawl is lowered to the sea bed to catch demersal fish it is referred to as 'Otter Trawling', and, when the trawl is between the surface and the sea floor to catch pelagic fish, it is referred to as 'Mid Water' or 'Pelagic Trawling'. The depth of the trawl is then controlled by the length of the haul line and/or the speed of advance. A 'Twin Rig Trawler' is capable of pulling two trawl nets with a third central haul line attached to both of the nets while the outer lines with the otter boards keep the nets open and apart. They are usually used for trawling on the sea bed. A 'Pelagic Trawler' pulls one very large trawl net which is kept open laterally by the otter boards and vertically by weights pulling the bottom of the Trawl downwards. It is used for catching mackerel and Herring and requires very powerful vessels. When two trawlers act together towing one trawl net between them it is known as 'Pair trawling'. The heavy otter boards that keep the net

Otter Board

Twin Rig Trawler - 2 nets and otter boards

open are no longer required, and because of the extra motive power available they can pull a larger net, and are also more manoeuvrable. They have had a lot of bad press recently due (a) to the number of dolphins which have been trapped in the larger trawl nets and (b) the damage done to the sea bed. Experiments continue to find net designs which overcome these problems. The boats generally have a crew of between two and four and will usually stay at sea for less than 24 hours.

"In the morning be first up, and in the evening last to go to bed, for they that sleep catch no fish"
(English Proverb)

Beam Trawlers   Beam trawling is a very efficient way of catching flat fish such as plaice, sole, turbot or brill. The bag like trawl nets are attached to heavy metal bars (Beams), which are suspended from derricks (booms) on each side of the vessel, lowered down (called 'shooting the nets') and dragged along the sea bed. The ends of the beams keep the net open and they can be towed at speeds up to 7 knots and so require considerable power. Without the restriction of the otter boards, they are not restricted to fishing in straight lines as the stern trawlers. They can also be used for shrimp trawling with lighter gear and at slower speeds. Generally they will trawl at depths up to 600ft, but it is possible to trawl at depths up to 4,000ft. The nets will be left down for up to two hours and then hauled. Beamers are generally larger boats and will often remain at sea for up to ten days. Unfortunately the gear can weigh up to 10 tons, and being so heavy they can leave considerable damage to the sea bed in their path. Deploying the booms out provides additional stability to the trawlers and even when in transit they will have them lowered out horizontally on each side.   Most of the beam trawlers in Cornwall are based in Newlyn, but because most of them were older vessels with powerful but fuel inefficient engines many have been scrapped or decommissioned in the last few years. The cost of running them with their quota restrictions and number of days limited at sea means that many have been retired reducing the beamer fleet in Newlyn from 31 in 2006 to less than 20 in 2013, despite some more modern boats replacing some of the older vessels.

**Derricks (Booms)
out for stability**

Beam Trawl Nets and Explanatory Diagram below

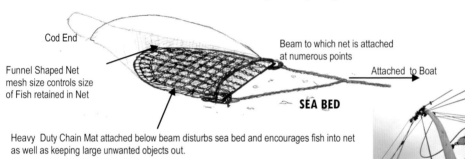

Cod End

Beam to which net is attached at numerous points

Attached to Boat

Funnel Shaped Net mesh size controls size of Fish retained in Net

SEA BED

Heavy Duty Chain Mat attached below beam disturbs sea bed and encourages fish into net as well as keeping large unwanted objects out.

If the trawl net catches in a protruding rock or a wreck on the seabed, it can put a considerable strain on the towing gear and it has even been known to cause trawlers to capsize. In the case illustrated (right) the derrick holding the beam had been put under such strain that it had been permanently bent and had to be replaced.

Scallopers These have similar equipment to the beam trawler but on a smaller and lighter scale. Instead of one net they have several scallop dredges which have rings or spikes to rake the seabed and net or metal bags to catch the scallops or shellfish as they are raked up. Smaller vessels may have as few as three or four dredges on each side while the larger vessels may have sixteen or more per side. Some vessels are designed solely for scalloping but many of the beamers and general purpose trawlers can be quickly modified in port to carry the scallop dredges. Scallops can be dredged from depths up to 90 fathoms but the deeper scallops tend to be smaller and less tasty. Scallop fishing is popular because there is a ready and lucrative market and there are no official quotas. Other fish are often caught in the scallop dredges known as by-catch but there are strict rules on how much can be kept, but fishermen suffer increased frustration at having to throw dead fish over the side just to satisfy quota rules. *(This may soon change, see p vii)*

Figure 3

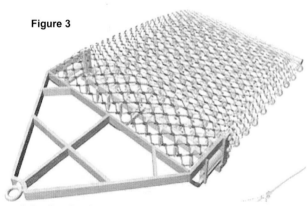

A Scallop Dredge - Crown copyright reproduced with permission

There may be several dredges shackled to a hollow steel tow bar (The Beam). Each dredge is fitted with a chain and bridle to attach it to the beam, and the whole assembly towed on a single wire warp. The vessels tow two beams one on each quarter and the number of dredges on each varies according to the towing power and manoeuvrability in the conditions. The picture below shows the beams and dredges deployed. Vessels with more than 4 dredges per side are limited to fishing offshore while the smaller boats with 4 or fewer are much less restricted. A few of the smaller boats tow up to three scallop

Several Dredges Shackled to the Beam

Rigged with 6 Scallop Dredges per side

Scallops—smaller *on right* is a ' Queen' scallop

dredges over the stern rather than from a beam over the side *(as shown below right)* The Scalloper *(illustrated below left)* shows part of a mechanism that some of the larger scallopers have for emptying the dredges of scallops. The area of the

side of the boat *(arrowed)* rotates upwards and 'teeth' attached to it catch on the scallop dredges forcing them to turn upside down emptying the scallops (and any other 'catch' - stones, fish etc.) on to a conveyor belt or hopper inside the boat. The conveyor system is not confined just to the larger boats as the photograph *(over)* indicates showing the conveyor belt on an under 10m scalloper.

Scallop dredges are changed according to the types of scallops which are to be fished. Queen scallops are smaller (around 3" across) as illustrated *(above)*. They are also good swimmers which means that they can be trawled as well as dredged unlike their larger relatives which are poorer swimmers and tend to seek crevices in rocks from which they must be dredged. A larger ring mesh is used for the King scallops *(illustrated in the centre over),* and a smaller ring mesh is employed in dredging for the queen scallops which are known as 'queenies'.

A single scallop dredge dismantled

The teeth on the rakes are set closer together or at smaller intervals apart on the bar when dredging for queen scallops compared with the larger scallops *(see pictures below)*

Conveyor belt to catch from the inverted scallop nets

Scallop dredge below
With close up on Right

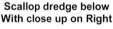

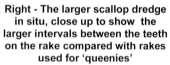

Above - A Pile of Queen Scallop rakes on the quayside waiting to be fitted.

Right - The larger scallop dredge in situ, close up to show the larger intervals between the teeth on the rake compared with rakes used for 'queenies'

Display on the Barbican at Plymouth with what is written *(arrowed)* shown below right

THE WAY OF ST JAMES

St James, one of the Apostles was martyred in AD44. Legend has it that he spent a number of years preaching in Spain and was subsequently buried there. His supposed burial site was discovered in the early 9th century and became a focus of pilgrimage. Hundreds of Thousands subsequently visited Santiago de Compostela. Many pilgrims sailed from England through Plymouth which was one of only two ports licensed for this journey. The pilgrims often wore a sign indicating their destination. Those going to Santiago de Compestala wore a scallop shell. This eventually became a general symbol of pilgrimage.

A well known scallop dish served in a scallop shell is 'Coquille St Jacques '*(Scallop of James)*. The scallop shell has always been associated with St James the Great. There are several legends attributing the origin of this, including one stating that the horse carrying the Saint's remains from Jerusalem to Spain fell into the water and emerged covered in scallops.

The scallop shell later became associated with all Christian pilgrims *(See bottom page xviii)*. Probably because of this, it has been incorporated in many coats of arms including those of the families of both Sir Winston Churchill and John Wesley, and thus the scallop shell also became the symbol of the Methodists.

> " *Give me my scallop-shell of quiet,*
> *My staff of faith to walk upon,*
> *My scrip of joy, immortal diet,*
> *My bottle of salvation'*
> *My gown of glory, hope's true gage;*
> *And thus I'll take my pilgrimage. "*

Thus wrote the great Elizabethan explorer and poet- Sir Walter Raleigh
(1552 –1618)

Many fishermen of all times have been discovered to hold an often private but sincere faith. Perhaps this comes of frequently facing the force of the elements. The adaptation of the 23rd. Psalm on the right reflects this.

Fisherman's 23rd Psalm.

The Lord is my Pilot. I shall not drift.
He lighteth me across the darkest waters:
In deepest channels- He steereth me.
He keepeth my Log. He guardeth me by-
the Star of Holiness, for His name's sake-
Yea thŏ I sail midst the thunder's and-
tempests of life : I will fear no danger, for Thou art
with me. Thy love and Thy care, they shelter me-.
Thou preparest a harbour ahead, in the haven of Eternity.
Thou anointest the waves with oil, my boat rideth calmly.
Surely, sunlight and starlight shall -
favour me, on all voyage's I take-.
And I will rest in the port of
my God forever.
Amen.

Gill Netters (Drifters) Drift netters carry a length of curtain like net which is let out (shot) from the stern and suspended from floats on the surface, as the boat travels downwind. The line holding the net is then taken round to the bow so that the drifter can lie head to wind. Tension is then kept on the line of net as the boat is blown downwind. Drift netters often carry a mizzen sail to help keep the boat into wind. Lengths of net vary but they may be several miles long in some cases. Such extreme lengths are unlikely to be used in the busy UK waters because of the risk of other vessels fouling the nets., and the average in Cornwall is about 3,000m.

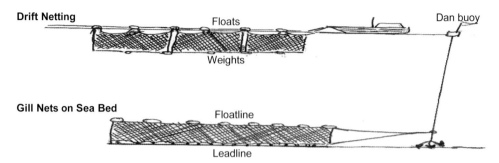

Netting over the many wrecks in Cornwall is popular where trawling is impossible. The fish are caught by catching their gills in the nets and there are strict rules on the sizes of mesh netting to be used for the type of fish to be caught, and to ensure that only mature fish are caught and not the young. Gill nets may also be set on the bottom as shown in the above diagram and marked with Dan buoys with red or black flags on them. Traditionally the flag on the most western buoy of the line of net is black and that on the eastern most is red. The top line is made of buoyant line called floatline and the bottom line called the leadline has lead weights enmeshed into it. When the nets are shot out by hand they pass over a steel frame on the stern as illustrated *(below left)* or by what is known as a net flaking device *(below right)*.

The nets are hauled using equipment traditionally installed on the starboard side forward of amidships. These come in many different forms but those illustrated below are typical.

Purse Seiner/Ring Netters & Seine Netters

These all have one thing in common in that, instead of waiting for the fish to swim into them, the gear is taken around a located shoal of fish to catch them.

Purse Seine/Ring Netters The net is shot round a located shoal in a circle. The net is then pursed (or closed) underneath the shoal by hauling in a wire which goes from the vessel through rings located at the bottom of the net and back to the vessel. The size of the purse is then reduced until the net is alongside and the fish are either scooped out called 'brailing' or

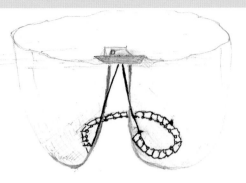

Purse Seine Net

Rigs used to deploy the Purse net

pumped out using fish pumps. The timing of each part of the manoeuvre to prevent the shoal escaping is critical. The mesh used is very fine so that the fish caught within the net are undamaged. Several older boats have been adapted for ring netting but some of them lack bow thrusters to give them the required manoeuvrability to close the circle and push the boat away from the net. These craft sometimes work with a smaller boat to help them in so doing. With the use of sonar to find the shoals, a modern ring netter can catch up to 78,000 pilchards valued at about £3,000 in a single trip. Presented as 'Cornish Sardines' they find a ready market in fashionable restaurants and they can be found in Marks & Spencers sold in small jars.

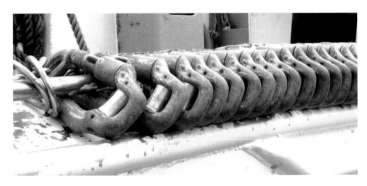

The rings awaiting deployment

Seine Netting This is a bottom fishing method particularly suited to flat sandy bottoms and is often used for demersal *(ground)* fish, such as cod, haddock and hake, and flat-fish like plaice and flounder. The end of one towing warp is buoyed and dropped overboard or held ashore. The fish are surrounded by motoring round the shoal in a large triangle as the warps (rope) are laid out on the seabed with a net with wings between them and returning to the buoyed warp. The boat then either anchors or moves slowly forward and as the warps are hauled in the fish are herded into the path of the net and caught. The warps' movement across the seabed results in a cloud of soft sediment, sand or mud assisting the process. This method of fishing yields a better quality catch, as the fish are not jolted on the bottom as with trawling. It is also more economical on fuel. This type of fishing is sometimes carried out from the shore using a small boat to take the net out as illustrated above.

Seine netting from shore

A Modern Seine Net

Ship at anchor hauls in ropes which herd fish into net.

Net wings 'Funnel' fish into net

Fish collect in cod end

The seine, or dragnet is well documented in ancient writings for instance by Ovid and the Bible, and is depicted on ancient Egyptian grave paintings of the 3rd century BC . Thus it must be the oldest type of commercial fishing net. The basic method seems to have changed little over the centuries and Ovid mentions the use of corks to support the top and lead weights on the bottom. The greatest change seems to have come in the past century with the introduction of modern synthetic fibres.

"Again, the kingdom of heaven is like a seine net which was thrown into the sea and gathered fish of every kind; when it was full, men drew it ashore and sat down, and sorted the good into vessels but threw away the bad." (Bible - Matthew 13:47-48)

Liners. 'Small Line fishing' may be carried out by hand or using poles suspended out from each side of the boat, but various specialized equipments have been developed for use on even the smallest of boats. Each line will carry several hooks on short branch lines called 'Snoods' which all have to be baited and laid out. Many modern hooks are now fitted with artificial bait to reduce the work load because it can be very hard work! The 'Longer Liners' require winch gear to haul in since they can have between 500 and 1,200 hooks spaced at one fathom (six feet) intervals. These are weighted at the bottom end to go down to, and along the sea bed and may be left for several hours anchored with a marker dan buoy. Fish caught by gillnetting often suffer gill damage which does not happen with fish caught on a hook, which is one advantage of line fishing. Fish so caught will be landed as quickly as possible. Most of the line fishing in the South West is 'Small or Long

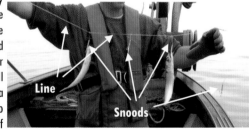

Line

Snoods

Mackerel hanging from the Snoods on the line

Lining' but 'Great Lining' uses much longer lines with up to 12,000 hooks and at depths up to 3000ft with fully mechanised baiting, shooting and hauling equipment. The small or hand liners generally use about 60 metre lines with between 20-40 snoods set at one metre intervals. Another development is the jigger liner which uses equipment to automatically jig the line up and down to attract the fish to the baited hooks. It is very effective with the artificially baited hooks.

**Lining Equipment
Stowed** (below) **&
in use** (lower left)

Rigged for jigger lining

Three large 'netters' from Newlyn have been adapted for long lining for tuna in the Bay of Biscay (Photo David Linkie)

Potters, Crabbers and Whelkers These are vessels which have the ability to carry a number of pots or creels which are laid on a continuous line with a marker buoy left at each end. Pots can be ink bottle shaped as in the centre pictures of the illustrations below, which are used mainly for crab. Creels are either rectangular or D-shaped as illustrated in the other pictures and are used for lobster. Whelks and prawn pots obviously must be of smaller mesh than those used for crab and lobster, and traditionally they were made of basket work. Today plastic, metal, wood and even polythene tubing might be used. The boats are fitted with a winch system to haul in the pots over some form of davit, usually fitted forward on the starboard side to keep the lines from the propeller. After leaving the baited pots down, ideally for about 24 hours, the pots are lifted in turn, the catch removed, pots re-baited and lowered back to the seabed again in one continuous action. Even small open boat potters may service as many as 250 pots while the larger potters may service as many as a 1,000 and possibly up to 2,000. Many potters are often fitted with large trays on the transom to carry the pots and the larger vessels will carry them below decks as well. The type of pots, and baits used, depends on whether the boat is used for lobsters, crab or whelks. Crabs require fresh bait whereas lobsters take stale bait. The crabs have to be measured using a standard measure to ensure that smaller juvenile crabs are returned to the sea. They are often stored in an anchored keep pot in clean unpolluted water just outside the port until sufficient quantity is available for sale. The claw tendons are nicked *(cut)* so that the crabs will not nip and damage each other while being stored in the keep pots. The number of potters operating in the county has dropped by half since 1995.

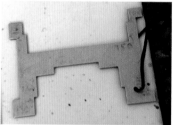
Typical Crab Measure

Crab Nicking Wedge in use

Examples of some of the Various styles of Pots & Creels that exist

Many of the modern vessels being built are designed as multi-purpose fishing vessels and can quickly be adapted to trawling, netting, potting or lining. Potting takes place all round the Cornish coast. The brown crabs and lobsters are mainly for UK consumption but most of the spider and velvet crabs are exported, and many are landed directly in France.

Unloading the Pots

Full Keep Pot about to be anchored

Examples of Changes in Fishing Boat Appearance
Spot the differences

Mevagissey based Fishing Vessel PW240

September 2005
(Then based in
Padstow)

February 2009
Dramatic Colour
change,
removal of stern
pot tray,
and fitting of
equipment for
netting

April 2013
Wheelhouse
moved forward
and to starboard
side with another
dramatic colour
change

Examples of Changes in Fishing Boat Appearance
Spot the differences

FY270 'Radjel' at Mevagissey from 2009 to 2012 - New Colour Scheme

PZ5 'Sou'Wester' at Newlyn from 2006 to 2013 - Subtle change of wheelhouse

SC73 'Steren Mor' on move from Scilly to Mevagissey from 2005 to 2012
New colour scheme & fitting of aft wheelhouse

SS65 'Hope' at Newlyn from 2011 to 2013 - New wheelhouse

Examples of Changes in Fishing Boat Appearance
Spot the differences

FY781 'Linda B' in Newlyn from 2005 to 2008
Wheelhouse changed and moved from Aft to Forward

FH57 'Foxy Lady' - New fittings & New Colour Scheme from 2004 to 2012

UL4 'Star of the North' to SC14 in Newlyn from 2008 to 2013
New Colour Scheme, Wheelhouse & Registration change

PZ1 Sarah Beth in Newlyn from 2006 to 2012
New side protection changing appearance completely

Historically, Cornwall's fleet was mainly based on drift and seine netting, aiming for pelagic (surface) fish, rather than trawling for demersal (ground) fish, and to some extent, this situation has continued. The demersal fish include plaice, sole, turbot, cod, pollack, eels and ling, while pelagic fish include mackerel, pilchards, bass, herring, hake and mullet.

Until the 1930s much of the fishing industry in Cornwall was based on the pilchard season. Huge pilchard shoals of up to 500,000 fish having wintered in the warmer waters south west of the Isles of Scilly moved north-

eastwards in July, and on reaching Lands End split north and south, moving along the North and South coasts of Cornwall. Because of this slow advance, catches could be anticipated as the shoals moved along the coast. The method of catching the shoals was fascinating. They were caught using seine netting in groups of three boats. One larger vessel - the 'Seine' - surrounded a shoal with the seine net, and dragged it into shallow water. This seine net was up to 1000ft long, 70 ft deep and weighed up to three tons. It was at the end of a one mile long three inch rope cable, by which the net when full was winched to the shore. The second smaller boat called the 'Follower' (sometimes corrupted as 'Follier' or 'Volyer') carried the 'stop or thwart net' to go under the shoal and lift the fish from the water. In East Cornwall a third faster boat called the 'Lurker' with the Master Seiner on board directed the operations. In West Cornwall this task was usually carried out from a lookout position on the shore by the 'Huer' using a form of semaphore signals. *(These signals bore some resemblance to the form of marshalling now used by ground staff to direct pilots taxiing aircraft on the ground!)* Such a group was known as a 'Seine', and in 1870 there

Huer's marshalling signals

were as many as 380 Seines in Cornwall alone. The majority of them were at St Ives, though only 71 of them were actually fishing in that year. At the height of the Pilchard era a Seine could catch as many as 13 million fish over a period of 8 days. The rota for which Seine should fish when the shoals were sighted was tightly controlled, and the order of fishing was determined by a Seine Boat Race before the season started!! (though each Seine got its turn). The pilchard season lasted from July to October and in many years provided a sufficient income for the whole year in that period alone. Since the mackerel season was from January to June, this fitted in well with the July to October pilchard season, so a good year could be very profitable. With the mackerel came the predatory and more valuable hake. These were caught by hand lining and made a further profitable sideline to the main mackerel fishing. From the late 19th century, the pilchards ceased coming in such numbers, and drift netting, for both pilchards and mackerel, gradually took over from seine netting. The last major seine 'enclosure' recorded off St Ives was in August 1908, and the last one recorded in Cornwall was off Porthcurno in Mounts Bay in 1916. There was considerable friction between the Seine fisherman and the Drift Netters since the Seiners blamed the Netters for preventing the fish coming inshore.

The industry employed huge numbers of people ashore, salting and packing the fish, and maintaining and building the boats and gear. The pilchards, after being left in a saline solution over periods as long as a year,

were carefully arranged radially, with the heads out *(as illustrated right)*, in barrels called hogsheads and then pressed down to dry them out and retrieve the pilchard oil which was used to harden the nets and waterproof the 'oilskins'. One hogshead contained about 3,000 fish and in the record year of 1871, 43,500 hogsheads were exported. This works out at about 130 million fish

A simple hogshead press

A Quarto hogshead

weighing approximately 10,000 tons. The main markets for the pilchards were in France, Spain, Northern Italy and even the Caribbean where they were paid for in rum!! As the demand reduced, the fish were packed in half

Pilchard press   **Pilchards pressed and Ready for Packing**

hogsheads or smaller quartos which contained only 300 fish, and they were also pressed into rectangular boxes for ease of transporting. Some of the fish were sold locally by women called 'Jowsters' who would wander the streets with a basket of fish on their backs, called a 'Cowell' and weighing about 70lbs. They also carried a further 40lbs of salt in a bag at the front.   The total is the equivalent of carrying a a hundredweight of coal!! Many of the historical fish cellars can still be found at the traditional fishing ports, though most of them have

been converted for other uses.   There is one fish cellar at Port Isaac which continues to be used for its traditional purpose with a fish shop and storage for fishing gear.   It is a surprise for many visitors to find that most of the fish on sale come from Newlyn market as the local boats are mainly used in potting for lobster and crab.   One of the cellars at Port Gaverne is still used for the storage of pots and fishing gear. Fishermen often lived above their fish cellars and many of the houses in St Ives have kept the names which reveal their original use.

Port Isaac fish cellar

Saltfish Cottage St Ives

When the last traditional salting works closed at Newlyn in 2005 it ended the 450 year old tradition of salting and pressing the pilchards in wooden cases going back to 1550.   Places where identifiable remains of the old fish cellars can be found include Kingsand, Polkerris, Coverack, Newlyn, Mousehole, Portloe, Port Isaac, Port Gaverne and Port Quin. In other places there is

little sign now of the industry that took place for centuries.   Although not in Cornwall, the 1336 Pilchard Inn sign on Burgh Island - west of Hope Cove - is the only remaining indication that there

was once a thriving pilchard industry on the island. Gradually ports have had to adapt to other types of fishing, though seine netting of the pilchards continues in the modern form of ring netting as described on page xxi.

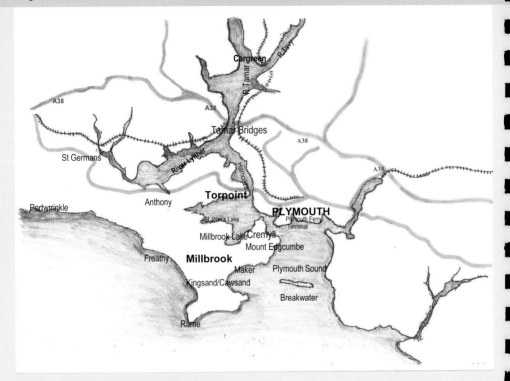

Since 1844 the River Tamar has been the natural border between Devon and Cornwall. Prior to this the Maker Peninsular (which includes Mount Edgcumbe) and the land between Millbrook Lake and St John's Lake actually formed part of Devonshire. Several boats, although nominally Plymouth based, are actually based between Saltash and Cremyll Point which are on the Cornish side of the river and will therefore be considered here.

Saltash was granted Borough status in the 14th Century and is therefore much older than the City of Plymouth. It was a major port and surprisingly had its own seine fishery despite being two miles upstream from the sea. Located at

St Germans Boatyard on the River Lynher

one of the two narrowest parts of the estuary it had a ferry service for several centuries until the suspension bridge was built in 1961. At the time of building the 1100ft span was the longest suspension bridge in the UK. Brunel's impressive railway bridge of unusual design was built 100 years earlier in 1859 and opened up Cornwall's fishing produce to London's markets. Plymouth based fishing boats have sometimes been seen passing Saltash on their way to carry out some oyster dredging up river. The River Lynher which joins the Tamar just south of Saltash has occasional visiting fishing vessels proceeding to the boatyard at St Germans for maintenance.

The main car ferry which is now at Torpoint dates back to 1791. The 'Karli N' (E20) was kept in the small marina downstream from the ferry slipway. This unusual square shaped marina, now connected to shore by a bridge, originally had a stone causeway

Ballast Pond Marina (*Devonport beyond*)
Both pictures

across to it and was built about 260 years ago as a 'Ballast Pond'. Barges supplied ships' stone ballast from inside the square and ships requiring ballast moored outside it. The means of transfer is rather obscure!!

Millbrook became established in 1867 from what was known as 'Maker'. The Maker parish covered most of the Rame Peninsular and in the 18th century the prominent Maker Church was used as a signalling station from the fleet in the Sound to the Devonport naval base. It is the only church officially allowed to fly the White Ensign. There was a small fishing fleet in Millbrook Lake in the 17th Century and Millbrook also developed thriving explosives and brickworks industries used by Devonport. It is now a quiet backwater but only a few fishing vessels continue to operate from the Southdown boatyard on Millbrook Lake, as several have transferred across to Plymouth. The old explosives barge which had been converted for use as a novel floating dry dock, has now been cut up and scrapped. The boatyard now concentrates on the maintenance of older wooden vessels. Boats entering Millbrook have to round Cremyll Point where the tidal currents can reach five knots

Towards the end of Millbrook Lake

Southdown Boatyard on Millbrook Lake

Southdown Fish Pontoon

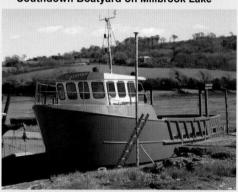
SD383 'Freedom' in the old 'Dry Dock'

on spring tides and cause quite choppy conditions. This is the location of the Cremyll passenger ferry from Plymouth to Mount Edgecumbe and Mashfords Boatyard. The Cremyll ferry was first documented in 1204 going back over 800 years and has been the scene of many incidents operating over such tricky waters! The boatyard, with five slipways, has been shipbuilding for some 200 years and continues to specialise in traditional boat building and maintenance. Fishing vessels up to 300 tonnes from ports in both Devon and Cornwall can sometimes be seen undergoing work in the yard. Although owned by DML of Appledore for several years it is now back in private ownership. In good summer weather some of the Millbrook boats can be seen moored offshore at Cawsand.

Entrance to River Tamar with Dockyard (on left) **and Mashford's Boatyard** (mid right)

RIVER TAMAR FISHING VESSELS

MILLBROOK (M), SALTASH (S), TORPOINT, (T)

P		PLN	Vessel Name	Type	LOA	Reg	Eng	Year	Hull	Nat
					Mtrs	Tons	Kw			Build
p	M	Ex CA6	LUNAR SEA	De-registered	7.80		81	1995	F	GBR
p	T	Ex E20	KARLI-N	De-registered	8.00	2.6	5	1978	F	
p	M	Ex E44	ARANDORA STAR	SANK 11/03/2012	8.5	3.7	59	1976	W	GBR
p	M	FY7	LITTLE MO	Liner	4.75		11.3	2005	F	GBR
p	S	Ex FY29	LITTLE FISHER	De-registered	8.8	6.7	33	1955	W	GBR
p	M	FY35	OUR MAXINE	Potter	4.56	0.67	11		F	GBR
p	T	Ex FY885	SAMUEL JAMES	De-registered	6.00	1.3	19	2007	F	PRT
p	M	Ex M111	KSH	To Plymouth	9.15	4.2	82	1981	F	GBR
p	M	Ex N303	ALBACORE	Houseboat at Millbrook	16.37	25	98	1970	W	GBS
p	T	Ex PE585	TWILIGHT	De-registered	5					
p	M	PH25	SULA BASSANA	Netter/Potter/Liner	8.20	3.6	60	1990	F	GBR
p	M	PH97	STELLA MARIS	To Plymouth (Ex CY192)	11.33	20	135	1988	W	GBR
p	M	PH307	SPLENDOUR	Potter	7.5	3	51	1988	F	GBR
p	M	PH585	SHIRALEE	Potter/Crabber	8.20	4.2	60	1963	W	GBR
p	M	Ex PH5595	UNCLE LEN	De-registered	9	2.6	81	1982	F	GBR
p	M	Ex PW121	ANNIE	De-registered	6.98	1.5	45	1987	F	GBR
p	M	SD383	FREEDOM	Trawler	10.00	9.5	95	2000	S	GBR

Ex CA6 Lunar Sea - 07/07/2010

Ex E20 Karli-N - 05/08/2009

Ex E44 Arandora Star - 31/10/2007

Ex FY29 Little Fisher - 25/05/2010

FY7 Little Mo - 06/08/2012

FY35 Our Maxine - 06/08/2012

Ex FY885 Samuel James - 12/05/2012

Ex M111(Ex PH11) **KSH** - 21/01/2011

Ex N303 Albacore - 18/10/2011

Ex PE585 Twilight - 21/01/2011

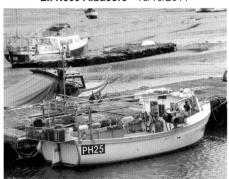

PH25 Sula Bassana - 06/08/2012

PH97 (Ex CY192) **Stella Maris** - 20/02/2010

PH307 Splendour - 02/06/2009

PH585 Shiralee - 18/10/2007

Ex PH5595 Uncle Len - 05/08/2009

Ex PW121 Annie - 31/10/2007

SD383 Freedom - 21/03/2007

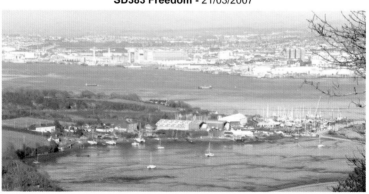

Millbrook Creek and Southdown Boatyard with RN Devonport beyond

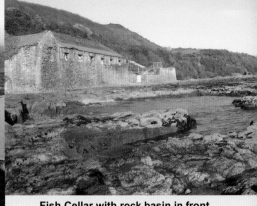

Fish Cellar with rock basin in front

Kingsand – Fish cellar on extreme right

The historic twin fishing villages of Kingsand and Cawsand once operated seven seines and a fleet of 40 drift netters at a time when the number of boats operating from Plymouth itself was only six. Most of them were pulled up on the beach at Cawsands as it was more sheltered than Kingsands. Kingsands was so named after Henry Tudor, Earl of Richmond, who was visiting the Earl of Edgcumbe while plotting to overthrow King Richard III, and evaded the King's men by escaping from the beach to a ship off Plymouth Sound in 1484. When he became King Henry VII in 1485 the beach became known as King's

Sand. The villages together formed an important fishing port until Plymouth developed in the mid 19th century and provided a more sheltered base from which to operate, and by 1914 there were only 16 boats in the villages. One of the old fish cellars can be seen on the coast just north of Kingsand. In front of the cellars a shallow basin has been cut out of the rocky shore line. Pier Cellars, just south of Cawsands and now owned by the MOD, was originally a fish cellar with its own tiny harbour. It was used as a training base for 'Human Torpedos' and mini-submarines during WW2. The 'Cawson' fishermen also had a profitable sideline in smuggling, and in 1804 it was estimated that 17,000 kegs of spirits were landed here illegally. The two villages are now well within the boundaries of Cornwall but this has not always been the case. The Devon/

The Slipway in Kingsands

Cornwall border until 1844 ran between the two villages, went to the north through the centre of what is now Millbrook, and rejoined the River Tamar at St John's Lake. Similarly a small area of the Devon side opposite Saltash belonged to Cornwall. This odd boundary line was formed so that the ferries operating across the Tamar, and between Plymouth and Kingsands would not have to pay taxes to two county authorities. No commercial fishing takes place now, but some of the Millbrook boats shown in the previous chapter can often be seen anchored off Cawsand in the summer months.

Old County
Boundary Marker
in Kingsands

Portwrinkle Harbour in Summer

The Harbour at High Water Spring tide

There is little shelter along Whitsand Bay between Plymouth and Looe, but Portwrinkle is a tiny harbour protected to some degree by a reef of offshore rocks. When it was built in 1605, the harbour walls stood much higher than they are now, but they have suffered four centuries of storms., and are now completely over run at high spring tides as the photograph above shows. In July of 1588, it was a fisherman from Portwrinkle, namely Sawney Bean, who first sighted the Spanish Armada and sailed round Rame Head into Plymouth Sound to advise Francis Drake of its approach. The fishermen from Portwrinkle were known as 'Wricklers' and there was much rivalry between them and the 'Cawson' men from Cawsands. Seine fishing was very active in the bay and the last recorded major catch was in 1935 when 3 tons of Bass were caught. There were reputedly a few small cellars along the coast of Whitsand Bay and the ruins of a cellar near Polhawn Fort are clearly visible but very inaccessible. There was a large 'Pallas' (a corruption of Palace) or fish cellar directly up from the Port itself. This was very much in ruins but the outer wall was sound and the outside steps up to the old accommodation could be clearly seen by the road. It has now been converted into very desirable accommodation. Only one small vessel still operates from the harbour during the summer months. Neptune is now de-registered and was last seen in Penzance harbour. Two small craft can also sometimes be found operating from the exposed slipway on the beach at Downderry along the coast towards Looe. They might otherwise be found operating out of Looe.

Modern descendants of Wricklers'?

Ruins of 'Pallas' - Fish cellar
(Now a smart apartment development)

PORTWRINKLE FISHING VESSELS

P	PLN	NAME	TYPE	LOA Mtrs	Reg Ton	Eng Kw	Year Built	Hull	Build Nat
p	Ex PH82	NEPTUNE	De-registered	4.4	0.8	3	1996	W	GBR
p	PH356	SCATHMAS	Potter	4.35	0.95	2	1976	F	GBR

Ex PH82 Neptune - 18/05/2005   **PH356 Scathmas** - 28/06/2006

Narrow approach channel to the harbour *(Note Marker beacon top right)*

Disused fish cellar near Fort Polhawn - Whitsand Bay

Looe Harbour & Bridge – Fish Quay on the right

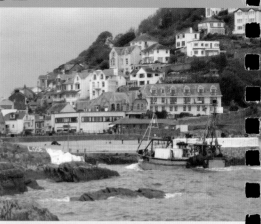

Mouth of River Looe & Harbour Entrance

Colourful line up

The twin towns of East Looe and West Looe received their separate charters as boroughs in 1571 and 1553 respectively, and they became one town only in 1898. Looe has a long fishing history. In 1656 five boats with eighty crew were lost to Turkish pirates while deep sea fishing between England and Ireland, and in the 19th century Looe fisherman would even venture as far as Newfoundland, fishing for cod. It was famed for its 60 strong fleet of luggers, drift netting for herring and pilchards in the summer, and long lining for turbot, conger and ray in the winter. The industry suffered from the collapses of the pilchard fishery in the 1930s and the mackerel fishery in the 1970s. Despite that, a fleet of some 50 small to medium size fishing boats still operates, with potting, long lining, trawling and scalloping being the main types of fishing, but charter angling is also popular here, and Looe is well known for game shark fishing. The size of boats has generally decreased with an increase in the numbers of small craft used for hand lining. Only 6 trawlers remain. It is one of the few UK fishing ports which lands what are known as 'Day caught fish', the fish being auctioned, within 24 hours of being caught. The fishing is mostly carried out within 40 miles from the coast between the Eddystone Reef and the Lizard. Most of the boats are Fowey (FY) registered, though several took advantage of registering in Wales but have since had to re-register.

The port is positioned at the mouth of the River Looe, which was canalised up to Liskeard in 1825. The canal closed in 1910 when the railways took over part of its course up the Looe Valley. Somewhat surprisingly, back in 1836, a large proportion of the total world's copper was exported through Looe, while the main import was lime for agriculture. The road bridge at the head of the port was originally built in stone as early as 1425. It was replaced in 1853 and widened in the 1950s. The seaward angle of approach to the River Looe, indicated by the beacon on the Banjo Pier, is critical as there are many rocky reefs just west of the entrance. The narrow entrance itself is protected by the 'Banjo Pier' but it is rather exposed in onshore winds, and though some protection is provided by the offshore Looe Island, flooding often occurs with a high spring tide, and there are strong tidal currents on both the ebb and flow. The harbour does not dry out completely, but access is limited to three hours either side of high water, and craft either lean against the quay at low water or are fitted with legs to remain upright. The embankment below the bridge on the West Looe side was opened with a final commemorative stone on 24th June 1931 by Prince George, later King George VI. The main fish quay and the fish market, built in 1987, are below the road bridge in East Looe, but fishing boats are found everywhere. Just inside the harbour entrance on the West side is a statue remembering 'Nelson' - a one eyed and scarred bull grey seal which made Looe Island and the harbour his home for 25 years until his death in 2003.

Banjo Pier Beacon

'Nelson' surveys all

LOOE FISHING VESSELS

P	PLN	VESSEL NAME	Type	LOA Mtrs	Reg Tons	Eng KW	Year Built	Hull	Nat
p	Ex AB226	FRANCIS FLO	De-registered	7.2	3	78	1997	F	GBR
p	BM367	BON ACCORD	To Plymouth	14.9	20.3	162	1968	S	GBR
p	BN447	TRADITION	Netter	6.14	1.2	18.7	2008	F	GBR
p	CK923	VICTORIA	Netter/Liner	9.90	7.5	209	1997	F	GBR
p	FH353	JANE LOUISE	Netter/Liner	7.75	5.9		1985	F	GBR
p	FH416	EMMA MAY	Netter	7.28	3.04	22	1977	F	GBR
p	FH484	TALLULA (Ex Tela)	Netter	7.62	5.1	13	1975	F	GBR
p	FY2	MEER	Netter/Liner	9.95	9.5	65	2007	F	GBR
p	FY5	FREYA JAE	Liner	5.85	2.10	19	2010	F	GBR
p	FY6	DOWNDERRY MAID	Liner	6.3	1.74	20	2010	F	GBR
p	FY24	ELLA	Trawler	11.3	19.3	223	1989	F	GBR
p	FY37	OUR GIRLS (Ex PZ682)	Liner	5.7	1.8	2	1980	F	GBR
p	FY38	MAXINE'S PRIDE	To Plymouth	11.9	28.5	273	1984	W	GBR
p	Ex FY44	NORVIK	SANK 11/04/11	7.9	3.9	22	1970	W	GBR
p	FY59	SWALLOW	Angler	11.7	8.4	158	1989	F	GBR
p	FY66	LUCY TOO	Netter	10.9	11.7	164	1989	W	GBR
p	FY97	GALATEA	Trawler	12.0	22.9	178	1984	F	GBR
p	FY120	SIRENE	Netter	6.5	3.4	26	1988	F	GBR
p	FY123	OHIO (ExSS689 & SA1238)	Angler	5.6	1.3	7	1985	F	GBR
p	FY124	KATYTU (Ex SA1240)	Netter	6.01	2.09	35	1989	F	GBR
p	FY228	ORCA	Potter	6.3	1	21	1989	F	GBR
p	Ex FY269	LEVAN MOR of LOOE	SANK 23/07/2008	10.8	11.6	170	1988	W	GBR
p	Ex FY302	LISANNE of LOOE	Decommissioned 09	9.75	9.9	72	1973	W	GBR
p	FY303	DISPATCHER	Crabber	6.1	2.6	41	1984	F	GBR
p	FY369	PARAVEL	Trawler	10.9	17.8	216	1979	W	GBR
p	FY523	MORDROS	Netter	9.23	9.34	53.7	1978	W	GBR
p	FY602	NATALIE	Trawler	11.3	15.7	178	1990	F	GBR
p	FY767	NEPTUNE'S PRIDE II	Liner	7.1	2.2	19	1993	F	GBR
p	FY778	TANEGAN (Ex LA778)	Potter	6.4	3.2	26	1996	F	GBR
p	FY804	PHOENIX	Netter/Crabber	9.98	5.6	45	1974	W	GBR
p	FY830	ATLANTIS	Trawler/Scalloper	9.9	10.2	115	2000	S	GBR
p	FY838	BOY'S OWN II	Liner	6	1.9	15	2001	F	GBR
p	FY850	TYPHOON	Net/Liner/Angler	9.9	5.2	195	2004	F	GBR
p	Ex FY857	OCEAN BLUE	De-registered	9.95	5.2	195	2004	F	GBR
p	Ex FY863	TEMERAIRE	De-registered	9.83	9.1	132	2005	F	GBR
p	FY869	MYSTIQUE II	Netter/liner/Angler	9.4	5.3		2005	F	GBR
p	FY892	TAMAHINE	Liner	4.8	0.7	5	1990	F	
p	FY894	HALCYON	Netter/Liner	8.2	72.0		2008	F	GBR
p	Ex FY898	MOOGIE	De-registered	6.1	2.2	24	2008	F	GBR
p	FY903	GUNGIR	Liner	5.7	1.26	42	2009	F	POR
p	FY917	BLUE MIST	Angler	6.52	1.61	85.8	2002	F	GBR
p	FY918	PANIA(ExFY960 & SA1239)	Angler	6.20	2.0	18	2003	F	GBR
p	FY920	JO JO LOUISE	Potter	5.6	1.05	17.9	1992	F	GBR

p	FY922	JUBILEE BELLE	Liner	6	2.58	18.7	1984	F	GBR
p	H22	SPURN LIGHT (Ex M21)	Liner	6	1.5	11	1986	W	GBR
p	Ex LT1	OUR BOY ANDREW	De-registered	10.0	17	100	1989	F	GBR
p	Ex M15	MARION (Ex FY569)	E15 @ Axemouth	4.4	0.7	1	1964	W	GBR
p	NN137	JOANNA	Trawler	14.0	20.3	179	1989	S	GBR
p	NN722	GUIDING LIGHT II	To Bideford	13.4	20.7	224	1988	W	GBR
p	PH584	MAID of KENT (Ex M584)	Liner	5	0.7	75	1986	W	GBR
p	PH601	CAWSAND BAY (Ex FH&PT601)	Netter/Potter	5.89	2.01	20	1991	W	GBR
p	PW473	VIDDY	Liner	4.91	0.3	6	1965	W	GBR
p	Ex PZ520	REWARD	De-registered	6.5	3.4	15	1987	F	GBR
p	PZ1202	GEMINI 2	Liner	4.8	1	10	2003	F	GBR
p	R159	MARET	Trawler	12.2	17.3	112	1963	W	DEU
p	Ex SA410	MOONRAKER (Ex SA118)	De-registered	5.9	1.04	15	2010	F	GBR
p	SM300	PEDRO	Liner	7	4.64	35	1972	F	GBR
p	SM799	CHARELLA of Shoreham	To Plymouth	11.9	37.2	221	1983	S	GBR
p	SS3	GUIDE ME	Liner	5.7	1.2		2005	F	GBR
p	Ex SS11	CHARISMA	To Plymouth	5.1	1.3	5	1989	F	GBR
p	SS284	JOHN WESLEY	To Plymouth	11.9	38.0	205	1981	F	GBR
p	SU515	CHARITY & LIBERTY	To Plymouth	14.9	40.1	221	2005	S	GBR
p	TH169	GERRY ANN	Trawler	11.7	20.4	159	1967	W	GBR
p	Ex WH6	CHERYL ANN	De-registered	5.72	1.65	18.7	1998	F	GBR

Note: LT1 was recovered to Fowey harbour after an accident which killed the skipper/owner

Ex AB226 (Ex FY808) **Francis Flo** - 09/05/2010

BM367 Bon Accord - 10/02/2010

BN447 Tradition - 09/03/2010

CK923 Victoria - 18/10/2011

FH353 Jane Louise - 09/03/2010

FH416 Emma May - 12/12/2007

FH484 Tela - 04/05/2010

FY2 Meer - 05/09/2012

FY5 Freya Jae - 05/09/2012

FY6 Downderry Maid - 29/03/2012

FY24 Ella - 27/10/2012

FY37 Our Girls (Ex PZ682 Helona) - 13/10/2012

FY38 Maxine's Pride - 31/03/2009

Ex FY44 Norvik - 16/04/2004

FY59 Swallow - 05/07/2012

FY66 Lucy Too - 09/03/2010

FY97 Galatea - 17/03/2008

FY120 Sirene - 05/09/2012

FY123 (Ex SS689 & SA1238) **Ohio** - 01/04/2013

FY124 (Ex SA1240) **Katytu** - 01/04/2013

FY228 Orca - 05/07/2012

FY242 Cornish Maid of Looe - 18/10/2011

Ex FY269 Levan Mor - 04/11/2003

FY303 Dispatcher - 09/04/2010

FY369 Paravel - 01/04/2013

FY523 Mordros - 27/10/2012

FY602 Natalie - 09/08/2006

FY767 Neptune's Pride - 17/10/2010

FY778 (Ex LA778)**Tanegan** - 05/09/2012

FY804 Phoenix - 17/10/2010

FY830 Atlantis - 05/07/2012

FY838 Boy's Own - 01/07/2008

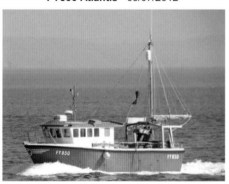

FY850 Typhoon - 30/03/2012

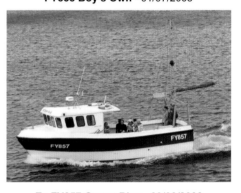

Ex FY857 Ocean Blue - 09/08/2006

FY863 Temeraire - 17/03/2008

FY869 Mystique II - 05/07/2012

FY892 Tamahine - 12/11/2008

FY894 Halcyon - 11/02/2009

Ex FY898 Moogie - 05/08/2009

FY903 Gungir - 05/09/2012

FY917 Blue Mist -13/10/2012

FY918 (Ex FY860 & SA1239) **Pania** - 25/04/2013

FY920 Jo Jo Louise - 25/04/2013

FY922 Jubilee Belle - 25/04/2013

16

H22 (Ex M21) **Spurn Light** - 14/10/2011

Ex LT1 Our Boy Andrew - 04/02/2009

Ex M15 (Ex FY569) **Marion** - 05/08/2009

NN137 Joanna - 18/10/2011

NN722 Guiding Light II - 27/08/2008

PH584 (Ex M584) **Maid of Kent** - 27/10/2012

PH601 Cawsand Bay (Ex Marley Lunn) - 05/09/2012

PW473 Viddy - 05/07/2012

Ex PZ520 Reward - 01/07/2008

PZ1202 Gemini II - 05/07/2012

R159 Maret - 05/07/2012

Ex SA410 (Ex SA118) **Moonraker** - 05/07/2012

SM300 Pedro - 18/10/2011

SS3 Guide Me - 30/03/2012

Ex SS11 Charisma - 09/05/2010

SS284 John Wesley - 09/05/2010

SU515 Charity & Liberty - 13/06/2007   **TH169 Gerry Ann** - 13/06/2007

Ex WH6 Cheryl Ann - 03/06/2011

Looe Entrance - as it was - and Now!

Looe Fish Quay

Smaller craft moored up below the bridge

West Looe Embankment Plaque

Polperro Entrance Gate looking West
Fish Quay on the left

The Outer harbour looking North East
(Central grey roofed building by the
waterside is the Heritage Museum)

Polperro from the Sea

Polperro is one of the most attractive fishing ports in the South West nestling in a small cleft in the rocky cliff shoreline where the River Pol runs into the sea. As well as running a highly successful pilchard fishing industry the village prospered even more on the results of smuggling contraband from the Channel islands. A school teacher called Zephania Job brought considerable organisation to this aspect of the village trade after his arrival at the end of the 18th century, so much so that he was able to open his own bank and finance the rebuilding of the port after severe storms in 1817 and 1824. The port is very exposed to winds from the south and in the major storm in 1817 it lost 30 of the 45 fishing vessels based in the port, and a further 19 boats in the storm of 1824. Although it took a long time to recover from these setbacks Polperro has continued to be a thriving fishing port. The harbour dries out almost completely at low water restricting entry to three hours either side of high water. The Eastern breakwater was built in around 1885, so that in bad weather timber baulks could be laid across the much narrowed harbour entrance. This protection was replaced in 1977 by a single lock type gate to keep the swell out of the main harbour. A varied fleet of some nine fishing vessels, netters and trawlers, operates from the port with several switching to hand lining for mackerel in the second half of the year. Several seines operated from Polperro and most of the harbour-side buildings housed fish processing cellars. One former pilchard processing plant is now the fascinating Heritage Museum of Fishing and Smuggling. Catches are landed at the quay on the inside of the main breakwater, and kept in the cold store on the south side of the Inner Harbour before being taken to Looe for marketing, but many owners land their catches direct in Looe to avoid paying the £80 transport fee from Polperro to the fish market in Looe.

The Outer Harbour looking North
The Fish Quay is in the foreground

POLPERRO FISHING VESSELS

P	PLN	VESSEL NAME	Type	LOA	Reg	Eng	Year	Hull	Build
				Mtrs	Tons	KW	Built		Nat
p	FY26	OCEAN QUEEN	Netter	8.3	59	52	1969	W	GBR
p	FY583	NORTHERN STAR II	Netter	7.80	3.7	26	1982	F	GBR
p	FY614	CAZADORA	Trawler	10.8	15.2	177	1985	W	
p	FY764	BOY WILLIAM	To Weymouth	6.32	2.18	12	1989	F	GBR
p	FY822	FAIR WIND	Netter	7.30	1.6	41	1999	F	GBR
p	P940	DAWN RAIDER	Netter	9.9	2.7	221	2002	G	GBR
p	PE474	KAREN	Trawler/Scalloper	9.97	13.4	119	1989	S	GBR
p	PH572	MY GIRLS	Netter/Potter	7.8	3.6	60	1992	F	GBR
p	PW75	PALORES	Netter	7.9	7.3	56	1980	F	GBR
p	Ex SD80	GIRL JANE	To Eire	11.6	15.2	94	1986	F	GBR
p	SU514	HOPE	Trawler	12.00	13.1	170	2003	W	GBR

Polperro's Sea Defences

FY26 Ocean Queen - 24/08/2009

FY583 Northern Star - 03/08/2007

FY764 Boy William - 09/03/2010

FY614 Cazadora - 01/04/2013

FY822 Fair Wind - 18/10/2011

P940 Dawn Raider - 01/04/2013

PE474 Karen Marie - 01/04/2013

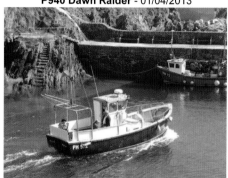

PH572 My Girls - 30/03/2012

PW75 Palores - 01/04/2013

Ex SD80 Girl Jane - 04/02/2009

SU514 Hope - 12/05/2012

Note: SU 514 is no longer based at Polperro but often seen in SW Waters

Polruan & Defence Tower (East Side of Entrance)   **St Catherine's Castle** (West Side of Entrance)

The River Fowey, originally called 'Foye', (as it is now pronounced) has an entrance like Dartmouth, that in the 15th Century used to have a protecting chain across it between fortifications on either side of the entrance. It was a major fishing port and in the 16th century Fowey fishing vessels were recorded as going across to Newfoundland for cod. It is a natural deep water harbour used by some surprisingly large ships. Freighters as large as 17,000 tons are manoeuvred up to the wharfs for the china clay industry above the Boddinick car ferry, and cruise ships up to 48,000 tons have visited the port. At first glance one would imagine that there are no fishing vessels in Fowey but a few can be found moored up opposite the clay wharfs, or moored close to Fowey town itself. Most of the Fowey (FY) registered boats are now based in either Looe or Mevagissey. Polruan, on the opposite side of the River Fowey from Fowey town itself, has a thriving fishing vessel construction and maintenance boat yard. It concentrates on wooden boats but many of the more modern steel vessels are fitted out here as well. Fish catches are landed by small boat tender to a ramp in the clay terminal and taken by road to the fish markets at Looe, Plymouth or Newlyn. Two or three boats can also be

found up the River Fowey at or near the attractive village of Golant. Here the construction of the railway embankment out in the river in 1869 left a sheltered creek inside the embankment called 'Golant Pill'. Draught and headroom are somewhat restricted however by the low railway bridge. The railway closed to passenger traffic in 1965. During the summer months these boats may be found moored in the river outside Golant Pill.

Off loading Fish from Tender

Fishing Vessels opposite Clay Wharfs

Polruan Boatyard

Golant Pill (Inside railway embankment)   **Railway Bridge at the Entrance to Golant**

FOWEY FISHING VESSELS

Photo	PLN	VESSEL NAME	Type	LOA Mtrs	REG TONs	Eng KW	Year Built	Hull	Build Nat
p	FY399	BLUE MARLIN	Netter	9.45	8.8	55	1975	W	GBR
p	Ex FY528	ANDORAY of LOOE	De-registered	7.7	4.7	41	1979	F	GBR
p	FY764	BOY WILLIAM	To Weymouth	6.32	2.2	12	1989	F	GBR
p	FY807	JESSICA GRACE	Trawler	9.7	9.29	119	1997	S	GBR
p	FY860	CORNISH LASS	Potter	9.95	10.2	374	2010	F	GBR
p	Ex FY866	CORNISH LASS III (ExBF267)	De-registered	9.98	5.7	374		F	
p	FY906	BLUE JAY	Netter/Liner	5.35	1.23	7	2003	F	GBR
p	LI559	PEPSI	Liner	5.52	2.2	20.9	2010	F	GBR
p	Ex PH600	LE BONHEUR	De-registered	8.9	4.52	89.5	1976	W	FRA
p	PH5547	OUR ROSEANNE	Scalloper	9.99	8.9	90	1999	S	GBR

FY399 Blue Marlin - 26/05/2006

FY528 Andoray of Looe - 09/04/2010

FY764 Boy William - 09/02/2010

FY807 Jessica Grace – 27/07/2009

FY860 Cornish Lass I – 11/06/2011

Ex FY866 Cornish Lass III - 09/04/2010

24

FY906 Blue Jay - 19/04/2013

LI559 Pepsi - 19/04/2013

Ex PH600 Le Bonheur - 11/06/2012

PH5547 Our Roseanne - 12/05/2008

The notorious smuggler/ fishermen the Carter brothers – one nicknamed the 'King of Prussia' - had two sides to their characters - as depicted by opposite sides of this pub sign by Fowey Quay

A large clay ship turns round in the harbour as seen from Polruan (A crowded Fowey main quay on the left) before reversing up the narrow channel top left to the clay quays

POLKERRIS

Tucked in the South East corner of St Austell Bay is the small harbour and hamlet of Polkerris. It was a major fishing port in the Pilchard era and the old salting and curing cellars are the largest in Cornwall, and can still be seen. The apparently castellated roof line is formed by the windows under a now collapsed roof. The village with only 70 houses once employed 300 people in the fishing industry. It was so important that the bay was then called Polkerris Bay. The southern breakwater was built in 1735, but when the outer harbour was completed at Mevagissey in 1888, that provided a much more sheltered base and fishing at Polkerris rapidly declined and ceased by the end of the 19th century. Even the lifeboat station was closed in 1922 when the boat was moved to Fowey. The oared lifeboat could not make headway against the strong tidal currents in Fowey harbour, but once fitted with engines the sheltered haven of the Fowey estuary was preferable.

Polkerris - Curing cellars on left

PAR

Fishing Boat Quay (Note sluice gate on left)   **Par Harbour**

Until Par harbour ceased being used as an outlet for the clay industry, access to the port was highly restricted, but despite that one fishing boat the 'Rosen' (BD252) had operated from the port for several recent years until late 2012. The name Par possibly originates from the 'bar' across the river entrance giving shelter to the small bay inside and providing a crossing place for the small river mouth. A Joseph Austen built the first bridge across the river mouth in 1824 and he went on to build Par Harbour. When construction of the harbour for the mining and china clay industries was started in 1829, Par was already a fishing port dating back to the 16th century and possibly before. Boats were drawn up on the beach with some of the houses, in what is now called Harbour Road, housing some of the fish curing cellars. Fishermen probably used the large fish cellars at Polkerris after the harbour was finished. The shore line then followed the line of the cliffs some ½ mile north of the present harbour which was built on reclaimed land. Construction of the harbour with three deep bays was completed in 1840 at the same time as a 2 mile tub boat canal was built northwards past St Blazey for the nearby copper mines and clay pits, inclined railways completing the journey. What is now the harbour sluice pond used to be the barge pool at the harbour end of the canal. The canal closed in 1873 and the subsequent railway was built along the towpath. The sluice pond was also used to flush out the harbour silt on an ebb tide. Tidal restrictions and a 16ft maximum draught limited use of the port, especially with Fowey nearby with its deep water harbour unrestricted by the tide. The last shipping cargo of china clay left Par in May 2008 and many of the buildings are gradually being demolished. Good quality sand from the clay pits is still being sorted at Par however, and exported using a private road and the railway to Fowey. Some of the huge drying sheds to the north west of the harbour are derelict and overgrown with greenery but a few are still in use, and some commercial clay activity still goes on There are plans for the harbour to be developed as a marina with up to 700 homes. There is little record of fishing more recently but there are now four registered boats using the harbour. One boat was built in 1939 and is one of the oldest active fishing boats in the South West. A temporary addition in 2011 was the LL272 'Jenna Lea' which was used on the mussel beds outside Charlestown.

Note: Clay Drying sheds on left
Fish quay top left and entrance to canal top right

PAR FISHING VESSELS

P	PLN	VESSEL NAME	Type	LOA	REG	Eng	Year	Hull	Build
				Mtrs	TONs	KW	Built		Nat
p	Ex BD252	ROSEN	De-registered	6.17	2	23	2006	F	GBR
p	FY887	PROVIDENCE	Liner	5.85	1	15		W	GBR
p	FY888	PAMELA JANE	Liner	6.90	1	21	1939	F	GBR
p	FY889	SCAVENGER	Shellfish dredger	4.12	0.35	5.9	1987	F	GBR
p	FY909	MERMAID	Dive boat	3.94	0.46	3	1991	F	GBR
p	Ex LL272	JENNA LEA	Mussel Dredger	12.95	17	216	1992	S	NLD

Ex BD252 Rosen - 13/10/2012

FY887 Providence - 11/06/2012

FY888 Pamela Jane - 11/06/2012

FY889 Scavenger - 12/10/2010

27

FY909 Mermaid - 13/10/2012

Ex LL272 Jenna Lea - 11/06/2011

8 CHARLESTOWN

Outer Harbour - looking East

Inner Harbour - looking South

Charlestown was built specifically for the china clay industry in the 1790s because it was the nearest place on the coast to the China Clay works above St Austell. It was financed by the mine owner Charles Rashleigh, and built by engineer John Smeaton, who also built the Eddystone Lighthouse. It was also used for the export of fish, and in 1847, 122M fish passed through the port. This industry died in the first half of the 20th century. Freighters up to 700 tons regularly visited the port to take on china clay until the late 1980s. Just three fishing vessels were using the outer harbour in the summer months, and during the winter Charlestown is a major maintenance base for several square riggers and traditional wooden craft. The entrance dries out, and there is little shelter to the south. After passing through the narrow entrance boats have to be warped round through ninety degrees in the awkwardly shaped outer harbour to align with the lock gates into the inner harbour. This difficult manoeuvre is well worth watching. The harbour entrance was widened in 1971 and a new 30.2 ton lock gate, which submerges rather than swing, was fitted before the harbour reopened in May of the same year. It is an attractive man-made port and full of interest, including the old china clay

Fishing vessels in outer harbour

loading facilities and the maritime museum. It was often used as a film set for historic films. In July 2012 the harbour and the 3 square riggers were up for sale for £1.4 million out of a total package of £4.4 million. In early 2013, the harbour was still for sale, but one of the vessels had been sold thus ending an era for Charlestown. The two potters had remained in their winter moorings on the river Fowey.

CHARLESTOWN FISHING VESSELS

Photo	PLN	VESSEL NAME	Type	LOA	REG	Eng	Year	Hull	Build
				Mtrs	TONs	KW	Built		Nat
p	FY777	FLYING SPRAY IV	Potter	8.13	6.27	237	1995	F	GBR
p	FY834	KATIE'S PRIDE	Potter	5.5	1.3	22	2001	F	GBR
p	FY884	TIMMY HAM	Dive Boat	4.01	0.5	10	2005	A	SWE
p	Ex SE70	CHANCE	De-registered	5.5	1.2	5	1992	F	GBR

FY777 Charltown - 09/04/2010

FY834 Katie's Pride - 05/08/2010

FY884 Timmy Ham - 11/06/2012

Ex SE70 Chance - 02/11/2007

Inner Harbour - Clay loading shute on left

29

Pentewan disused Lock Gate from the Basin

Pentewan Breakwater and silted up Channel
(Note 1910 extension to original length)

Between Charlestown and Mevagissey is the manmade, and now abandoned, port of Pentewan. Before the harbour was constructed, seine fishing took place from Pentewan Beach, and then continued after the harbour was constructed, but fishing ceased around the turn of the 19th /20th century following a legal dispute with the harbour authorities over a seine net fisher which had capsized in the harbour entrance. The original small harbour was built back in 1740, and the present harbour was completed in 1826 to rival Charlestown for the china clay industry. Silting up problems in the entrance marred a reasonably successful commercial career. In 1862 sixteen vessels were trapped for five weeks by the channel silting up, despite an ingenious system of reservoirs designed to flush out the harbour channel. The breakwater was extended in 1910 to try and alleviate the problem, but the last freighter visited in 1940. The lock gates were last replaced in 1911 but although they were rebuilt and the channel re-dredged after WW2, the harbour was never a success and allowed to silt up. There are possible plans to restore it for leisure use.

1826 'Foundation' Stone

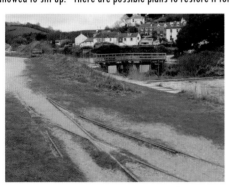

Railway lines, Lock Gate and Silted Channel

Conduit from reservoirs used to flush out the Channel

The basin with lock gate in distance

Restored sluice gate used to control flow from reservoir

Mevagissey Inner harbour looking NW

Outer Harbour Looking North

Mevagissey (named after St Meva & St Issey) is the largest traditional fishing port in the South West dating back to the 14th century, and despite its use as a busy commercial fishing port it retains a certain charm. Although one of the closest ports to the metals and china clay mining areas it was developed solely as a fishing port. In the 19th century, thirty 'Seines' were operating from the port, landing as many as 14 million pilchards per year. There is a large outer harbour where many of the craft are moored, and a drying out inner harbour which is filled with fishing vessels of all types. Although in the lee of the prevailing SWly winds, it is very exposed to the east. The first pier was built in 1430, and the inner harbour was enclosed in 1774. Most vessels then moored in the bay outside the harbour but they all had to cram into the small harbour when easterly gales were expected. The walls surrounding the outer harbour were originally built in 1888, but were destroyed by gales in 1891 and rebuilt in 1897. There are about 70 boats of all types, trawlers, netters, potters and long liners, but only eight are over 10m length. Many of the potters may service up to 500 pots each. Most of the boats carry the Fowey (FY) registration. Ring netting has become more popular and the ill fated 'Heather Anne' had been recently converted for that type of fishing. Most of the fishing is within 30 miles offshore, but some of the larger boats may even round Lands End and be away for several days. Recent fish landings have been at their highest quantity ever, having overtaken Looe, in terms of value of catches landed, for the first time. After local refrigeration the catches are taken to the fish markets at either Looe, Plymouth or Newlyn. Unlike many UK fishing ports there are still many young men coming into the industry, and with the port handling its maximum number of fishing craft, it is very much a thriving port with a very positive future.

Inner harbour looking South West

Fish Quay in foreground - looking North East

MEVAGISSEY FISHING VESSELS

P	PLN	VESSEL NAME	Type	LOA Mtrs	Reg Tons	Eng Kw	Year Built	Hull	Build Nat
p	BD18	GEMINI	Netter	7.13	2.36	31	1980	F	GBR
p	BH9	VALHALLA	Trawler	10.7	16.4	169	1989	W	GBR
p	FH25	SOVEREIGN	Netter/Potter	8.02	7.2	59	1983	W	GBR
p	FH52	STILL WATERS (Ex B522)	Trawler	9.87	10.5		1990	S	GBR
p	FH76	GALWAD-Y-MOR	Netter	11.9	21.7	120	1984	W	GBR

p	FH109	MARIA Q	Netter/Potter	8.1	4.2	80	1981	F	GBR
p	FH339	THREE BOYS	Netter/Potter/Liner	5.5	1.8	8	1976	W	GBR
p	FH693	LIZY	Netter	9.97	5.2	194	2000	F	GBR
p	FH715	KIMBERLEY JO	Netter/Liner	6.53	1.44	10.1	1978	F	GBR
p	FY8	SEA SPRAY	Liner	4.95	1.49	7.46	1980	F	GBR
p	FY9	BREEZE	Liner/Tender	5.2	0.73	11	2002	F	GBR
p	FY10	CELTIC DAWN (Ex WK10)	Netter/Ring Netter	13.45	27.8	129	1983	F	GBR
p	FY12	OCEAN HARVEST (Ex SY5)	Trawler	11.4	14.2	94	1985	F	GBR
p	FY15	FOUR MAIDENS (Ex M896)	Tender	4.30	0.6	15	1989	A	GBR
p	FY17	KINGFISHER of LOOE	Trawler	10.3	9.9	95	1983	W	GBR
p	FY19	CHRISTINE	Liner	6.7	3.6	16	1948	W	GBR
p	FY43	LENTEN ROSE	Trawler	9.98	6.4	82	1959	W	GBR
	FY52	C.J.		3.81	0.45	3	1972	F	GBR
p	FY53	DEMELZA	Netter	8.2	5.6	44	1970	W	GBR
p	FY58	VENUS	Netter	9.95	10.2	160	1992	F	GBR
p	Ex FY63	KERRY JAYNE	Decommissioned 09	9.1	7.4	59	1969	W	GBR
p	FY81	RUBY (Ex FY829 & M1188)	Liner	4.5	O.66	7.3		F	GBR
p	FY88	BUCCANEER	Netter	8.4	5.9	72	1970	W	GBR
p	FY91	MANX RANGER	Trawler/Scalloper	13.95	38	209	1991	S	GBR
p	FY108	TRUST (Ex PD108)	Liner	7.4	1.3	4	2009	F	POR
p	FY111	RED VIXEN	Netter/Potter	10.4	9.7	94	1986	W	GBR
p	Ex FY126	HEATHER ANNE	SANK 20 Dec 2011	11.0	11.7	164	1971	W	GBR
p	Ex FY156	CHARM	De-registered	5.6	1.7	7	1983	F	GBR
p	FY201	IBIS	Netter/Liner	5.9	1.9	32	2007	F	GBR
p	FY222	FREDDIE B	Liner	6.06	1.1	44	2011	F	PRT
p	FY270	RADJEL	Netter	6.6	2.8	24	1988	W	GBR
p	FY278	PUFFIN	Trawler/Liner	7.4	4.4	41	1989	F	GBR
p	FY324	AQUILA	Netter/Potter	9.4	7.5	140	1974	F	GBR
p	FY332	TAMARA	Netter/Liner	8.5	4.3	22	1965	W	GBR
p	FY345	LIVER BIRD	Netter	6.4	2.1	7	1980	F	GBR
p	FY367	INVESTOR	To Scarborough	9.75	9.7	95	1989	S	GBR
p	FY368	MAJESTIC	Potter/Liner	7.77	4.5	29	1977	F	GBR
p	FY400	MAKO	Liner	8.0	2.7	41	1958	W	GBR
p	FY431	LIBERTY	Netter/Liner/Angler	8.1	5.1	37	1966	W	GBR
p	FY470	IMOGEN (Ex PZ100)	Trawler	10.4	24	187	1991	W	GBR
p	FY509	SUPERB II	Netter	8.53	7.67	55	1978	W	GBR
p	FY523	MORDROS	To Plymouth	9.23	8.78	54	1978	W	GBR
p	FY555	LYONESSE	Potter	7.1	2.4	67	1987	W	GBR
p	FY588	BOY JOE II	Liner	4.8	1.5	8	1978	F	GBR
p	FY606	VESPER II (Ex FY30 & M606)	Netter	6.5	2.7	22	1988	W	GBR
p	FY755	GIRL AMANDA	Netter	6.2	2	18	1982	W	GBR
p	FY759	SURPRISE	Netter	6.72	2.17	22	1992	F	GBR
p	FY803	VERONA (Ex WAVE II)	Liner	5.4	1.6	7		F	UNK
p	FY811	MARY EILEEN	Liner	4.8	1.4	4	1986	F	GBR
p	FY817	SAMMY JAYNE	Potter	4.8	0.8	11		F	UNK
p	FY823	CONWAY	Liner	4.7	1.3	9	1989	F	GBR
p	FY826	SUNSHINE	Netter/Liner	6.4	3.0	30	1999	F	GBR

MEVAGISSEY FISHING VESSELS cont'd

p	FY836	LAUREN KATE	Netter	9.95	5.5	138	2001	F	GBR
p	Ex FY837	JIMINI K	De-registered	3.9	0.6	4	1985	F	GBR
p	FY841	DEMPER	Netter	4.9	0.8	15	2000	F	GBR
p	FY842	JACOB	Tender	3.86	0.6	14	1998	F	GBR
p	FY843	LUCY B	Netter	4.30	0.54	10	-	F	
p	FY848	DEFIANT	To Southampton	13.95	30.0	221	2004	S	GBR
p	Ex FY864	BLACK PEARL	Decommissioned 09	6.54	3.1	30	2005	F	GBR
p	FY868	CORNISHMAN	Netter/Liner	5.85	0.8	13	2003	F	GBR
p	FY872	MORGELLAN	Liner	6.10	1.5	16	1980	W	GBR
p	FY875	CRIMSON TIDE	Netter	5.94	1.0	33	2006	F	GBR
p	FY881	PETREL	Liner	6.25	1.8	14		W	GBR
p	FY886	AVOCET	Liner	4.60	0.3	11	1980	F	GBR
p	FY890	MOLLY MAI	Liner	4.80	0.6	7	2000	F	GBR
p	FY913	MARY ANN	Liner	4.15	0.64	14.7	1996	F	GBR
p	Ex M115	BOA PESCADOR (Ex WH115)	De-registered	8.10	4.60	89	1972	W	GBR
p	Ex M896	FOUR MAIDENS (Ex FY896)	De-registered	4.30	0.6	15	1989	F	GBR
p	Ex MN199	SOLSTICE	De-registered	9.90	9.20	119		S	
p	Ex MN203	TONKA	Decommssioned	5.88	1.1	34	2004	F	GBR
p	NN135	BREAKING DAWN	Trawler/Netter/Potter	9.6	6.8	89	1988	F	GBR
p	Ex P483	ABILITY (Now SM75)	To Shoreham	11.5	20.8	146	1990	S	GBR
p	PH959	RICHARD ANN	Netter/Ring Netter	9.99	9.9	112	1996	F	GBR
p	PW240	DILIGENCE	Netter/Potter	8.65	3.9	86	1975	W	GBR
p	PW362	CHARLOTTA	Scalloper/Netter	7.98	4.1		1979	F	UNK
p	PZ17	CARISSA ANN (Ex Newlyn)	Liner	6.36	2.5	28	1997	F	GBR
p	PZ87	KATIE CLAIRE	To Ilfracombe	13.45	21.6	218	1997	S	GBR
p	PZ118	PENDOWER (Ex PZ1183 St Ives)	Liner	5.59	1.8	7	1992	F	GBR
p	PZ495	JACKIE MARIE	Netter/Liner	5.6	1.51	11	1978	F	GBR
p	Ex PZ594	STORM PETREL	De-registered	4.5	0.7	7		F	GBR
p	SC27	ISIS	Netter	7.6	5	38	1980	F	GBR
p	SC60	LEONORA	Netter/Liner	6.6	3.3	26	1982	F	GBR
p	SC73	STEREN-MOR (Ex Pioneer II)	Netter	6.71	0.95	21	1989	F	GBR
p	SE322	CARPE DIEM	To Brixham	5.9	1.1	10	1989	F	GBR
p	SS5	KLONDYKE	Liner	5.5	0.7	3	1985	F	GBR
p	SS173	RHIANNON JANE	Netter	5.9	2.2	14	1980	F	GBR
p	SS233	TRYPHENA	Liner	5.63	1.44	10.1	1978	F	GBR
p	SS683	MARLIN G	Netter/Liner	6.1	1.8	31	1996	F	GBR
p	SU513	CHALLENGE	Trawler/Scalloper	9.98	14.29	131	1997	F	GBR
p	TO6	ALANA TROY	Liner	4.86	1.1	11	2009	F	GBR
p	Ex UL580	RESOLUTE	De-registered	5.6	1.63	10	1989	F	GBR
p	WH324	LIKELY LAD (Ex Saundersfoot)	Potter	9.85	6.06	95		F	GBR

Note: PZ495 'Jackie Marie' fishing
from Gorran Haven in 2013

**The rocky coastline
outside the harbour**

BD18 Gemini - 11/06/2012

BH9 Valhalla - 09/09/2012

FH25 Sovereign - 11/06/2012

FH52 (Ex B522) **Still Waters** - 21/03/2012

FH76 Galwad-y-Mor - 25/04/2013

FH109 Maria Q - 09/09/2012

FH339 Three Boys - 19/04/2013

FH693 Lizy - 05/07/2012

FH715 Kimberley Jo - 09/09/2012

FY8 Sea Spray - 19/04/2013

FY9 Breeze - 19/04/2013

FY10 (Ex WK10) **Celtic Dawn** - 25/04/2013

FY12 (Ex SY5) **Ocean Harvest** - 09/09/2012

FY15 (Ex M896) **Four Maidens** - 19/04/2013

FY17 Kingfisher of Looe - 21/10/2008

FY19 Christine - 19/04/2013

FY43 Lenten Rose - 11/06/2012

FY53 Demelza - 05/08/2009

FY58 Venus - 11/06/2012

Ex FY63 Kerry Jayne - 12/02/2009

FY81 (Ex M1188) **Ruby** - 19/04/2013

FY88 Buccaneer - 11/06/2012

FY91 Manx Ranger - 23/03/2013

FY108 (Ex PD108) **Trust** - 09/09/2012

FY111 Red Vixen - 221/05/2007

Ex FY126 Heather Anne - 26/11/2010

Ex FY156 Charm - 21/10/2008

FY201 Ibis - 05/08/2009

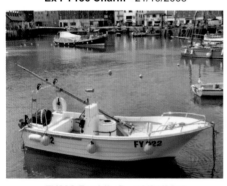

FY222 Freddie B - 19/04/2013

FY270 Radjel - 09/09/2012

FY278 Puffin - 05/08/2009

FY324 Aquila - 09/08/2012

FY332 Tamara - 12/02/2009

FY345 Liver Bird - 25/04/2013

FY367 Investor - 24/08/2007

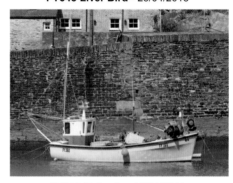

FY368 Majestic - 19/04/2013

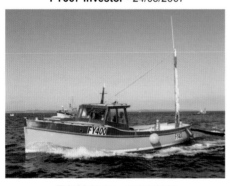

FY400 Mako - 24/08/2007

FY431 Liberty - 05/08/2009

FY470 Imogen (Ex PZ110) - 09/08/2012

FY509 Superb II - 11/06/2011

FY523 Mordros - 31/05/2007

FY555 Lyonesse - 09/08/2012

FY588 Boy Joe II - 11/06/2012

FY606 (Ex M606) **Vesper II** - 19/04/2013

FY755 Girl Amanda - 11/06/2011

FY759 Surprise - 11/06/2011

FY803 Verona - 11/06/2011

FY811 Mary Eileen - 12/11/2010

FY817 Sammy Jayne - 11/06/2011

FY823 Conway - 14/03/2010

FY826 Sunshine - 05/08/2009

FY836 Lauren Kate - 11/06/2011

Ex FY837 Jimini K - 05/08/2009

FY841 Demper - 24/08/2007

FY842 Jacob - 19/04/2013

FY843 Lucy B - 02/05/2007

Ex FY846 Bella Margaret - 21/05/2008

FY848 Defiant - 25/04/2013

Ex FY864 Black Pearl - 21/10/2008

FY868 Cornishman - 12/10/2010

FY872 Morgellan - 11/06/2012

FY875 Crimson Tide - 25/04/2013

FY881 Petrel - 21/03/2012

FY886 Avocet - 12/02/2009

FY890 Molly Mai - 14/03/2010

FY913 Mary Ann – 11/06/2012

Ex M115 (Ex WH115) **Boa Pescador** - 14/03/2010

Ex M896 (Ex FY896) **Four Maidens** - 05/08/2009

Ex MN199 Solstice - 11/06/2011

Ex MN203 Tolka - 02/05/2007

NN135 Breaking Dawn - 12/02/2009

PH959 Richard Ann - 19/04/2013

PW240 Diligence - 19/04/2013

PW362 Charlotta - 12/02/2009

PZ17 Carissa Ann - 25/04/2013

PZ87 Katie Claire - 26/01/2009

PZ118 (Ex PZ1183) **Pendower** - 02/03/2009

PZ495 Jackie Marie – 19/04/2013

Ex PZ594 Storm Petrel – 21/03/2012

PZ882 Sea Lion - 19/04/2013

SC27 Isis - 19/04/2013

SC60 Leonora - 26/11/2010

SC73 Steren-Mor - 19/04/2013

SE322 Carpe Diem - 30/08/2007

SS5 Kondyke - 09/09/2012

SS173 Rhiannon Jane - 05/08/2009

SS233 Tryphena - 09/09/2012

SS270 Zara - 19/04/2013

SS683 Marlin-G - 19/04/2013

SU513 Challenge (Ex Faith) - 13/10/2012

TO6 Alana Troy - 19/04/2013

Ex UL580 Resolute - 11/06/2011

WH324 Likely Lad - 19/04/2013

A crowded Inner
Harbour

Gorran Haven looking towards Chapel Point

Gorran Haven was originally known as Porth East. It is three miles south of Mevagissey with Chapel Point between them. It has a small harbour with a single breakwater and superb beaches in the lee of Dodman Point. Until the 19th century Gorran was busier than Mevagissey, and it was a busy fishing port right up until the 1970s. Early records show that there was a small fishing haven here in the 13th Century and a stone quay in the 15th century. A further quay was built in 1825 and there was a thriving pilchard seine industry in the village which employed half the working population of the village. The other half was employed in farming. The present quay was built by the local squire between 1885 and 1888, and little has changed except that the sea has destroyed the fishermen's toilet in the corner where the quay turns from the east to the north. A fishermen's Cooperative operated from 1917 to 1970, with the catch housed in the store by the slipway and taken daily to St Austell station by road for onward marketing. There were as many as 40 crabbers operating from the port at times during this period. The harbour provides little protection during strong winter easterly winds, but six small boats still operate from here through the Spring to Autumn months potting, netting and lining, with some charter fishing in season. Some of the boats may be seen in nearby Mevagissey during the winter months or stored in the old fishermen's compound in the shelter of the low cliffs. Even in the summer they sometimes move to Mevagissey from a security angle with the huge number of tourists on the harbour beach and wall.

Gorran Haven looking south

Boat Store and Old Fish Cellar

GORRAN HAVEN FISHING VESSELS

Photo	PLN	VESSEL NAME	Type	LOA Mtrs	Reg Tons	Eng Kw	Year Built	Hull	Nat Build
p	CS295	KATY	Liner	4.4	0.8	3	1975	F	GBR
p	FY1	THREE JAYS	Netter/Potter	4.8	1.1	15	2004	F	GBR
p	Ex FY4	FULMAR	To Portree	4.9	1.0	10	2004	F	GBR
p	FY14	SHAKIRA	Netter/Potter	4.23	0.6	19	2011	A	GBR
p	FY174	EMBLEM	Liner	4.6	0.8	7	1989	F	
p	FY545	JENNY JAMES	Netter/Potter	3.8	0.6	3	1972	F	GBR

Note: In 2013 Mevagissey boat PZ495 'Jackie Marie' was doing most of her fishing from Gorran Haven

CS295 Katy - 30/05/2006

FY1 Three Jays - 24/08/2007

Ex FY4 Fulmar - 24/08/2007

FY14 Shakira - 19/04/2013

FY174 Emblem - 24/08/2007

FY545 Jenny James - 21/05/2008

47

12 PORTHOLLAND

East Portholland Bay

Portholland East and West are small hamlets with only 40 permanent residents, and a few old fisherman's cottages, which were described by John Betjeman as 'Summer hide-outs'. It is protected to the east by the prominent Dodman's Point on which a local parson placed a Cross as a daymark for shipping in 1896. There are two separate coves at high tide, but at low tide they are linked by a sandy beach. It has great appeal to those wishing to escape the commercialism of the 21st century with only a single small shop and Post Office. Apart from the new sea defences the hamlets have remained unchanged for over a hundred years evoking nostalgia for the Cornwall of long ago and have been declared National Heritage Assets. They no longer show much of their fishing heritage however.

13 PORTLOE

The Slipway

Portloe Harbour looking North East

Portloe is just two miles south east of Portholland, at the head of a small 'L' shaped inlet at the western end of Veryan Bay. It is dramatically squeezed into a steep valley, as are many of the typical Cornish harbours. It provides reasonable shelter in most weathers but is rather exposed to an easterly blow, and looking at the harbour entrance it is hard to imagine how at one time it supported a successful seine fishery and a small drift fleet. Old photographs of about 1890 show the beach filled with small craft. The old fish cellars can be found behind the Post Office and are still used by the fishermen for storage. It is a small, unspoilt fishing village with few houses and a shingle beach. Today only two fishing boats operate from the cove, lobster and crab potting, servicing up to 400 pots, with some netting for various species and hand lining for mackerel in season. These are the same two boats that were seen here in the late 1960s! On calm sunny days the sea here is a beautiful turquoise colour. Mullet can be seen swimming by the short harbour wall, but the path on to it is steep and could be dangerous, especially for children.

Like many of the Cornish ports, Portloe has a smuggling history which is said to have been centred on the 17th century Inn which is now the Portloe 'Lugger Hotel'. A former landlord, known as Black Dunstan, was hanged for smuggling in the 1890's. This finally put paid to its trade as licensed premises, and it fell into disrepair, and at one time acted as a boat builder's shed, before its renovation and re-licensing in 1950. There is an attractive 'Figurehead' on a building overlooking the bay.

I see no Ships!

The 'Fleet' at low water

PORTLOE FISHING VESSELS

P	PLN	NAME	TYPE	LOA	Gross	Eng	Year	Hull	Build
				Mtrs	Tons	Kw	Built		Nat
p	FH75	JASMINE	Potter	5	2	14	1982	W	GBR
p	Ex FH711	BLUEBELL	De-registered	4.4	1	22	2002	F	GBR
p	FY180	KATIE LIL	Potter	6	2	17	1986	F	GBR
p	Ex PD1034	ZEPHRON (Ex FH712)	De-registered	5	1	45	2000	F	GBR

FH75 Jasmine - 02/11/2007

Ex FH711 Bluebell - 02/11/2007

FY180 Katie Lil - 17/03/2007

Ex PD1034 (Ex FH712) **Zephron** - 17/03/2007

PORTSCATHO

Portscatho Harbour & Slipway

On the eastern side of the Roseland peninsular is Gerrans Bay and in the Bay's south western corner is Portscatho which means 'Boat Cove'. It lies sheltered in the lee of the prevailing south westerly wind, in close proximity to Gerrans village which is higher up and slightly more inland. The two villages are closely linked but have maintained a considerable good natured rivalry. The Portscatho breakwater which gives some protection to the east was built in 1891, and the sea walls protecting the village have rather attractive and unusual sloping paths leading down to the breakwater and the beach slipway. Seining was a feature of Gerrans Bay fishing for centuries and in 1626 eighteen seines were recorded as operating in Portscatho, although some drift netting was later carried out in the 19th century. The seining peak came in 1908 when enough fish were caught to fill 1,478 hogsheads totalling some 4,435,000 pilchards. In 1910 the three seines still operating formed the 'Covers Seining Co', with a legal document laying down the rules of how the seines should operate without interfering with each other. Seining was still being carried out in 1923 but gradually declined as the pilchard numbers decreased. The fish cellars were situated behind the present post office, but are no longer there. In the 1970s

Dried out!

mackerel were appearing in sufficient numbers for a new seine to start up which employed twelve people, but fishing has gradually declined, and now only four people remain commercially fishing from Porthscatho, netting, lining and potting from three cove boats.

Curious tales are told of 'sea serpents' caught in fishermen's nets in Gerrans Bay in 1876 and also in 1926. These were described as around 20ft long with an 8ft tail, scaly legs and a beak-like head. There were very few recorded sightings until the 1970's when more were apparently seen but no photographs ever seem to have been taken!!

Gerrans Bay also provided good shelter for smuggling in the 18th century from the Revenue men. Posted lookouts on the surrounding hills could give ample warning of any approaching revenue cutters.

It is surprising to find, just above the harbour in Portscatho, the only memorial of its kind dedicated in memory of the 26,380 men with no known grave who were killed in Burma in WW2. That it is here, is due to the fact that James Allen a veteran of that campaign retired to Portscatho and in 1998 at the age of 84 years, his long held ambition to see such a memorial erected was fulfilled .

The 'Burma Star' Memorial

Portscatho at high tide in Winter

Portscatho at Low Tide in Summer

PORTSCATHO FISHING VESSELS

P	PLN	VESSEL NAME	TYPE	LOA Mtrs	Gross Tons	Eng Kw	Year Built	Hull	Nat Build
p	FH3	ROSEN	Potter	6.17	2	23	2006	F	GBR
p	FH4	ROSE (Ex FH686)	Potter	4.7	1.25	16	1992	F	GBR
p	FH23	IONA	Netter/Liner	4.5	0.8	7.7	1998	F	GBR

FH3 Rosen - 21/05/2008

FH4 (Ex FH686) **Rose** - 09/08/2012

FH23 Iona - 09/08/2012

Breakers at Portscatho

Falmouth Old Harbour (Docks beyond)

Falmouth Waterfront

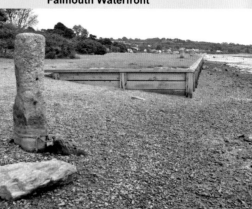

Abandoned Quays at Devoran
(Top of Restronguet Creek)

The Fal Estuary is the world's third largest natural harbour formed as a drowned river valley or 'Ria'. Following the Spanish raids on the fishing ports of Mousehole, Penzance, and Newlyn in 1595, the defences into the Fal estuary were improved with the construction of St Mawes and Pendennis Castles. Penryn and Truro, being nearer to the major tin mining areas, were the major ports in the estuary until about 1820, when the port of Devoran was developed to serve the increasing demands of the mining industry. Penryn had been established in 1216, and was then the major port for both the local mines and the export of granite stone. Falmouth itself, which was originally known as Smithwick, only became a major port after Sir Walter Raleigh recommended its development in 1613. King Charles 2nd decreed that it should be known as Falmouth in 1660. As the size of vessels increased, the importance of both Truro and Penryn decreased, since they were unable to handle the larger vessels. The Custom House was then moved from Penryn to the new port of Falmouth. Devoran, at the top of Restronguet Creek, was closer to the mining areas and continued commercial operations, but it gradually silted up and was abandoned in 1915. It was served by the 1826 Redruth & Chasewater Railway which was horse drawn until 1854. The residents of Falmouth were the first UK citizens to officially receive the news of Nelson's victory at Trafalgar. Lapenotiere, who commanded the schooner 'HMS Pickle', brought home the news of Nelson's death and his victory at the Battle of Trafalgar (21st October 1805). He landed in Falmouth after a record passage time with his official dispatches on Monday 4 November 1805, from where he took a fast coach to London and the Admiralty. Because of Falmouth's sheltered location in the lee of The Lizard it was a favourite departure point for ships west bound, and the first port of call when inbound. Truro was however the main commercial centre in the area and continued as the major port until Falmouth took over, though small cargo vessels still reach the outskirts of Truro. As a major customs town/city Truro became one of the fishing registration ports despite there being little fishing activity from the city itself. Falmouth and Flushing were the home of the 'Falmouth Packets' carrying mail across the globe from 1688 to 1850, but after the advent of the railways and introduction of steam propulsion, the 'Packet' owners favoured ports nearer to London. Fishing prospered and the 'Fish Strand Quay' in Falmouth itself was built in 1790. Most of the development of the Falmouth docks took place from 1860 onwards. St Mawes was the major fishing port in the Fal Estuary supporting a thriving pilchard, potting and oyster industry but there is little sign of that in the village now, though several fishing boats moor offshore. The pier here dates back to 1536, though it was improved in 1854 and rebuilt in 1873. During WW2 the Fal Estuary was effectively closed to civilian movements, and it was a major US departure point for the D-Day landings at Omaha Beach. Operation 'Chariot' - the highly successful raid on the French dock at St Nazaire using the old destroyer HMS Campbeltown - also departed from here on 28th March 1942. A slightly reduced and varied fishing fleet of some 38 vessels now operates from several points around the estuary with Flushing, Penryn, Mylor, Restronguet and St Mawes being the main places at which fishing vessels can be found, as well as in the small harbour close to the main fish quay in Falmouth itself, which has the 'Old Customs Quay'. Oyster fishing still goes on using the traditional sailing smacks and rowing punts to avoid pollution. It is managed through the Truro Port Fishery Order. The boatyard at Mylor Bridge carries out maintenance and construction work on many fishing vessels from all around the Cornish coasts. From Falmouth to The Lizard most boats bear the Falmouth (FH) registration.

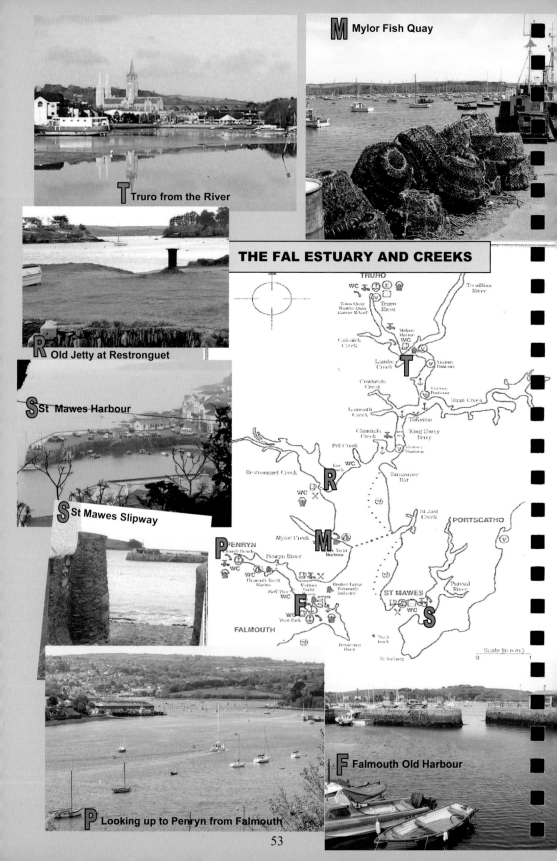

M Mylor Fish Quay

T Truro from the River

R Old Jetty at Restronguet

S St Mawes Harbour

S St Mawes Slipway

THE FAL ESTUARY AND CREEKS

F Falmouth Old Harbour

P Looking up to Penryn from Falmouth

53

Falmouth Custom House   **St. Mawes Castle**

Mylor with Oyster Catcher (sail)   **Oyster reels and dredges**

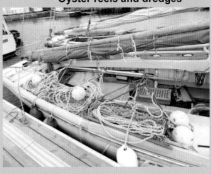

Oyster Catchers at Mylor

New pontoons at Penryn

FALMOUTH FISHING VESSELS

FALMOUTH(F) St MAWES(S) MYLOR(M) PENRHYN(P) TRURO(T) RESTRONGUET(R)

P		PLN	VESSEL NAME	Type	LOA Mtrs	Reg Tons	Eng Kw	Year Built	Hull	Nat Build
p	S	FH2	TREVALLY	Potter/Liner	7.65	4.52	44.2	2007	F	GBR
p	S	FH6	CELESTIAL DAWN	Trawler (Ex UL2)	11.4	15.1	94	1988	F	GBR
p	S	FH7	GENEVIEVE	Netter	6.2	1.7	83	2006	F	GBR
p	S	Ex FH8	RHODA MARY	De-registered	8.38	3.6	8	1980	F	GBR
p	F	FH12	MOREL MARGH	Scalloper	10.9	9.8	220	1989	S	GBR
p	M	FH17	NIKI LOU	Angler	6	1.23	51.5	2012	F	GBR
p	M	FH51	AMIGO (Ex FR51)	Potter	7.62	2.75	37	1979	S	GBR
p	F	FH55	PATRICE II	Netter/Liner	7.78	5.07	179	1988	F	GBR
p	F	FH58	BILLERIC	Potter	5.56	1.8	13	1978	F	GBR
p	M	FH85	SCATH DU	Potter	6.8	3.72	26	1982	F	GBR
p	R	FH89	CARIAD	Jigger Liner	7.3	2.6	24	1989	F	GBR
p	M	Ex FH178	MAGDALENA	De-registered	6.77	3.46	18	1969	W	GBR
p	F	Ex FH206	GOLDEN FLEECE	Now MT99 N Shields	13.9	22.2	187	1975	W	GBR
p	F	FH207	GOLDEN FLEECE II	Scalloper	14.95	42.2	221	2007	F	GBR
p	F	FH300	PAULA ROSE	Potter	7.19	2.29	27	1980	F	GBR
p	S	FH322	BOBBIE DEE II	Trawler/Scalloper	10.8	14.7	96	1975	F	GBR
p	M	FH395	TRENEGLOS	Netter	8.05	3.37	89	1977	F	GBR
p	F	Ex FH442	PROPERJOB	De-registered	4.66	1.17	8	1978	F	GBR
p	P	FH443	SOLITAIRE	Netter	6.49	3.18	22.3	1976	F	GBR
p	F	FH485	LEVIATHAN	Potter/Liner	9.94	7.96	74	1979	F	GBR
p	S	FH598	GIRL RACHAEL	Trawler	9.91	12	164	1991	F	GBR
p	F	FH609	DOMAR (Ex M609)	Potter	4.24	0.6	4	1991	F	GBR
		FH638	ELA-J		6.81	22.4	48	1996	F	GBR
p	M	FH664	AMETHYST	Scalloper	9.9	9.95	125	1998	S	GBR
p	M	FH665	REBECCA	Scalloper	9.97	11.47	97	1991	F	GBR
p	M	FH669	MARIA 2	Netter	7.13	1.58	20	1997	F	GBR
p	M	FH690	PETER JOHN II	Netter	8.02	3.17	101	1999	F	GBR
p	P	Ex FH700	REBECCA	Decommissioned 2009	4.9	1.1	6		F	
p	M	FH702	CORNISH LASS	Liner	8.25	4.26	63	1989	G	GBR
p	T	FH705	HOBBIT	Netter	5.88	2.21	30	1980	G	GBR
p	M	FH714	FRANCES B	Potter	7.29	4.7	45	1983	F	GBR
p	S	Ex FH716	RUBY TUESDAY	De-registered	4.61	0.85	4.4	1997	F	GBR
p	R	FH722	PROPHET	Potter	6.85	2.7	31	2000	F	GBR
p	M	FH723	HARVESTER II	Netter/Potter	11.83	12.8	136	2004	F	GBR
p	P	FH729	JACQUELINE ANNE	De-registered	10.94	12	221	2005	S	GBR
p	M	Ex FH730	FIONA STARR	To Jersey	9.33	5.1	130	2000	F	GBR
		FH733	FLOWER OF FAL		5.49	1.4	8	1981	F	GBR
p	M	FH734	PATRICIA ANNE	Potter	5.82	1.8	12	1984	F	GBR
p	P	FH740	REBECCA TOO	Netter	5.75	1.87	13.5	1980	F	
p	F	FH745	MORVRAN	Liner	5.8	0.9	56	2007	F	GBR
p	M	FH748	SAPPHIRE	Angler	6.68	2.92	85.8	2003	F	POL
p	M	FY96	AQUAMANDA	Netter	8.12	5.07	32	1980	F	GBR

55

P		Reg	VESSEL NAME	Type	LOA	Reg	Eng	Year	Hull	Nat
					Mtrs	Tons	Kw	Built		Build
p	P	Ex FY226	NOR'ROCKER	De-registered	9.75	10.3	90	1962	W	GBR
p	S	PE820	AVON VALLEY	To Holyhead	12.3	12.4	139	1980	W	GBR
p	R	PH74	ON WARD	To Plymouth	5.64	2.2	11	1971	W	GBR
p	M	PW440	FINNISH GIRL	Angler	5.98	.7	52	1998	F	GBR
p	M	PZ353	GIRL PENNY	Netter/Potter	9.91	7.5	44	1972	W	GBR
p	S	PZ642	SERENE	To Beer	5.88	2.08	13	1979	F	GBR
p	M	RX189	BRAVEHEART(Ex OB89)	To Rye	9.9	13.5	131	1991	S	GBR
p	M	Ex SA30	GIRL LUCY	Not registered	5.55	1.29	15	1971	W	GBR
p	M	SS759	MAXINE CHARLOTTE	Liner	5.2	1.19	67.1	2006	F	GBR
p	M	TO4	ZONA	Mussel-Dredger	4.3	0.57	3		W	UNK

FH2 Trevally - 09/08/2012

FH6 (Ex UL2) **Celestial Dawn** - 09/08/2012

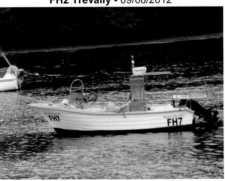

FH7 Genevieve - 15/07/2008

Ex FH8 Rhoda Mary - 03/01/2011

FH12 Morel Margh - 03/03/2011

FH17 Niki Lou - 13/03/2013

56

FH51 (Ex FR51) **Amigo** - 21/03/2012

FH55 Patrice II - 17/02/2009

FH58 Billeric - 12/03/2013

FH85 Scath Du - 17/02/2009

FH89 Cariad - 21/03/2012

Ex FH178 Magdalena - 13/10/2012

Ex FH206 Golden Fleece - 17/03/2007

FH207 Golden Fleece II - 13/10/2012

FH300 Paula Rose - 21/03/2012

FH322 Bobbie Dee - 14/03/2010

FH395 Treneglos - 21/03/2012

Ex FH442 Proper Job - 14/04/2008

FH443 Solitaire - 12/03/2013

FH485 Leviathan - 13/10/2012

FH598 Girl Rachael - 17/02/2009

FH609 (Ex M609) **Domar** - 14/04/2008

FH664 Amethyst - 12/03/2013

FH665 Rebecca - 13/10/2012

FH669 Maria 2 - 21/03/2012

FH690 Peter John II - 12/03/2013

Ex FH700 Rebecca - 24/08/2007

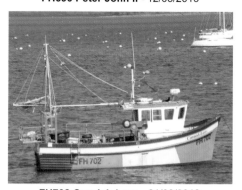

FH702 Cornish Lass - 21/03/2012

FH705 Hobbit - 12/03/2013

FH714 Frances B - 21/03/2102

Ex FH716 Ruby Tuesday - 17/03/2007

FH722 Prophet - 09/07/2012

FH723 Harvester II - 12/03/2013

FH729 Jacqueline Anne - 24/08/2007

FH730 Fiona Starr - 17/03/2007

FH734 Patricia Anne - 14/03/2010

FH740 Rebecca Too - 12/03/2013

FH745 Morvran - 21/03/2012

FH748 Sapphire –13/03/2013

FY96 Aquamanda –13/03/2013

Ex FY226 Nor'rocker - 15./07/2008

NN94 Semper Fidelis - 17/02/2009

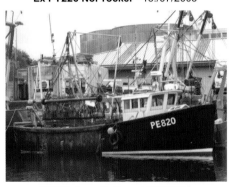

PE820 Avon Valley - 11/08/2011

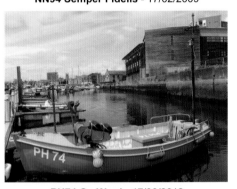

PH74 On Ward - 17/06/2012

PW440 Finnish Girl - 22/11/2005

Ex PZ74 Sanluro - 29/08/2009

PZ353 Girl Penny - 21/03/2012

Ex PZ459 Celtic Lass - 13/02/2007

PZ642 Serene - 07/01/2012

RX189 (Ex OB89) **Braveheart** - 31/10/2012

Ex SA30 Girl Lucy - 13/03/2013

SS759 Maxine Charlotte - 13/03/2013

TO4 Zona - 21/03/2012

Helford Passage

Looking West up River

The Helford River is considered to be one of the most attractive river estuaries in the UK. It is also home to what was one of the the UK's oldest ports. Gweek at the head of the estuary was a port as far back as 450BC, and was still active in the 19th century, after which its use declined as the river silted up. It is now a large boatyard for winter storage and maintenance. The River has no coastal defences such as found with Pendennis and St Mawes Castles in nearby Falmouth, and in the 16th century there were several reports of the river being used as a haven for English, French and even Dutch pirates!! A pilchard fishery was established at the picturesque village of Helford in the mid 19th century. The old harbour at Helford is now disused and the pilchard cellars and sail lofts nearby have been converted into attractive accommodation. The estuary provides a sheltered anchorage for up to a dozen small to medium sized fishing craft and innumerable private yachts. There is no quay to which vessels can go alongside, and ferries or tenders provide the means of getting ashore to either Helford village on the south side or Helford Passage on the north side. Catches are landed by tender at Helford and taken by road to Newlyn fish market. Discussions have been going on to improve the landing facilities for fishermen, but there are some who fear any change would spoil the natural beauty of the area. Oysters and mussels continue to be farmed further up river and in the creek up to Porth Navas opposite Helford village. Two or three vessels can be found at Bishop's Quay near the village of Mawgan, and several craft are kept in the attractive inlet just south of the entrance to the river known as Gillan Harbour with the hamlets of St Anthony, and Gillan north & south of the entrance and Flushing at its western end, but in the winter the boats often shelter well up the inlet.

Looking across to Helford Passage
(From the Old Harbour at Helford)

Old Harbour at Helford

Helford River entrance looking to the east

HELFORD RIVER FISHING VESSELS

P	PLN	Vessel Name	Type	LOA Mtrs	Gross Tons	Eng Kw	Year Built	Hull	Nat Build
p	FH5	PERSEVERANCE Ex REGINA MARIS	To Scarborough	12.38	19.2	213	1994	W	GBR
p	FH9	AMANDA J	Potter/Liner	5.9	1.6	20	1999	F	GBR
p	FH60	NEW HARMONY	Netter	9.6	13.04	112	1995	F	GBR
p	FH88	KARENZA JAYNE	Netter	6.62	1.41	26	1986	F	GBR
p	FH187	KON-TIKI	Netter	4.3	0.69	2	1980	F	GBR
p	FH214	LADY HAMILTON of Helford	Netter/Liner	8.53	6.73	96	1972	W	GBR
p	Ex FH726	LADY LYNDA	De-registered	7.3	1.8	54	1975	F	GBR
p	FH728	STERENNYK	Netter/Liner	9.95	6.8	118	2005	F	GBR
p	FH750	MYGHAL	Netter/Liner	8.47	8.4	134	2008	F	GBR
p	FH756	EMILY JAYNE	Netter	9.15	4.72	53.6	1999	F	GBR
p	FY239	LUCY MARIANNA	Netter	9.14	4.9	60	1973	W	GBR
p	NN27	BONNIE GRACE	Netter	7.74	2.17	52	1984	F	GBR
p	Ex PE888	LADY MATILDA	De-registered	9.2	5.67	89	1982	F	GBR
p	Ex PT601	Ex Marney Lunn	To Looe as PH601	5.89	2.15	20	1991	W	GBR
p	PW81	JULIE GIRL	Netter/Liner	8.15	2.5	61	1980	F	GBR
p	PW228	MA-VIE	Netter	8.74	6.19	90	1977	W	GBR
p	Ex PZ13	I'LL TRY	To 3 Rivers S Wales	5.5	1.67	7	1979	F	PRT
p	PZ14	LITTLE LAUREN	Liner	4.87		11	2011	F	GBR
p	PZ67	PEDDEN	Liner	4.8	0.71	11	1980	F	GBR
p	PZ280	TALISMAN	Netter/Liner	9.33	7.01	32	1965	W	GBR
p	Ex PZ1221	BAND OF BROTHERS	De-registered	5.78	1.91	18		F	GBR
p	SS67	TRACEY CLARE	Netter	9.94	5.91	95	1980	W	GBR
p	Ex SS685	FOU DE BASSAN	De-registered	5.46	1.02	11.2		F	
p	WY335	SAEDIA LOUISE	To Bridlington	10.9	19.5	150	1982	F	GBR

The Lady Hamilton (FH214) was involved in a serious collision in poor visibility at the mouth of the Helford River on 3rd October 2007 with a boat Blythe Spirit (FH683) coming from Falmouth and the Lady Hamilton was capsized and sunk. She was recovered and restored at Gweek boatyard, and was re-launched on 17th March 2008.

"The fishermen know that the sea is dangerous and the storm terrible, but they have never found these dangers sufficient reason for remaining ashore"
Vincent Van Gogh

FH5 Perseverance (Ex Regina Maris) - 03/10/2007   **FH9 Amanda J** - 03/10/2007

FH60 New Harmony - 12/03/2013

FH88 Karenza Jane - 21/01/2006

FH187 Kon-Tiki - 21/01/2006

FH214 Lady Hamilton - 12/03/2013

Ex FH726 Lady Lynda - 03/10/2007

FH728 Sterennyk - 12/03/2013

FH750 Myghal - 31/07/2009

FH756 Emily Jayne - 12/03/2013

FY239 Lucy Marianna - 03/10/2007

NN27 Bonnie Grace - 12/03/2013

Ex PE888 Lady Matilda - 02/03/2009

Ex PT601 (Ex FH601) **Marley Lunn** - 06/10/2010

PW81 Julie Girl - 12/03/2013

PW228 Ma Vie - 22/04/2006

Ex PZ13 Ma-Nicks - 03/10/2007

PZ14 Little Lauren - 12/03/2013

PZ67 Pedden - 09/07/2012

PZ280 Talisman - 06/10/2010

Ex PZ1221 Band of Brothers - 14/04/2008

SS67 Tracey Claire - 12/03/2013

Ex SS685 Fou de Bassan - 03/10/2007

WY335 Sardia Louise - 03/10/2007

Gillan Harbour (Dodman Point in distance)

Porthallow Beach - Cellars in Distance   **The Thatched Cottage**

Porthallow, known locally as 'Pralla', is an old pilchard fishing village in a small bay north of The Lizard Peninsula, and south of the Helford River. The old fish cellars can be seen on the southern side of the beach. The two 'Toshers' remaining that operate from here are hauled up onto the rather exposed shingle beach in front of an attractive thatched cottage. The beachside pub called 'The Five Pilchards' is a reminder of fishing days past, but why only 'Five'? The pub has a sizeable collection of old photographs and shipwreck relics. Walks from Porthallow provide magnificent views of Falmouth Bay and the general coastline but the southwest coastal path is routed inland from here because of the nearby quarries for local stone which were much favoured for road building, but now mainly disused. An Observation Post for the anti submarine torpedo range on nearby Nare head operated until 1994. Despite all three boats having re-registered with Welsh *(Milford M)* registrations to minimise quota restrictions, only two of them now remain registered and both back with local registrations.

PORTHALLOW FISHING VESSELS

P	PLN	VESSEL NAME	Type	LOA Mtrs	Gross Tons	Eng Kw	Year Built	Hull	Nat Build
p	FH119	SEA URCHIN (Ex M1193)	Liner	4.76	1.21	13	1988	F	GBR
p	Ex M597	BOY BRAD (Ex FH657)	De-registered	4.8	1.16	13	1989	F	GBR
p	PZ462	AYLISHIA (Ex M462)	Potter/Liner	5	0.86	11	1972	F	GBR

FH119 (Ex FH611 & M1193) **Sea Urchin** - 06/10/2010

Ex M597 (Ex FH657) **Boy Brad** - 09/04/2010

PZ462 (Ex M462) **Aylishia** - 19/10/2010

Disused Stone Mill

Beach with Stone Quarry Opposite

Porthoustock (pronounced locally as 'Proustock') lies in a small bay on the sheltered side of The Lizard. Historically it was a small fishing hamlet, and then developed as a port in the 1890s for the nearby quarries, which despite recent talks about closing them, were still in use in 2013. Vessels of up to 82 metres LOA can get alongside on the southern side of the harbour. A large disused stone mill and quay on the north side provides some shelter from the east. The shingle beach is actually reclaimed land and the old lifeboat house at the head of the beach was originally right by the shore line. Only seven small craft continue to operate from the shingle beach, mainly lining, but a few potters and netters as well. There is a row of huts in the shelter of the land to the east which provide storage space and contain motorised winches to haul craft back up the beach, though a tractor is also used. The menacing 'Manacles Rocks' just to the south of Porthoustock have claimed thousands of nautical victims and the fishermen of the port were often busy manning the local lifeboat as well as fishing. Around 1900 there were many well documented shipwrecks in which the Porthoustock lifeboat played a major part. It was withdrawn in 1942. The 'Manacles' Reef is also a good line fishing location for bass in the summer months.

The fleet hauled up above the high water mark (Note the sheds for the winches and storage)

PORTHOUSTOCK FISHING VESSELS

P	PLN	VESSEL NAME	Type	LOA Mtrs	Gross Tons	Eng Kw	Year Built	Hull	Build Nat
p	FH200	JEN-LOU II	Netter/Liner	5	0.88	3	1978	W	GBR
p	FH293	GIRL PAULINE	Netter/Liner	5.28	1.26	10	1983	F	GBR
p	Ex FH340	TAMALIN	De-registered	5.03	1.13	9	1971	W	GBR
p	FH468	GIRL JAN	Netter/Potter/Liner	6.30	2.64	22	1979	F	GBR
p	FH613	KERANY (Ex M613)	Liner	4.75	1.08	7	1991	F	GBR
p	LO540	BANANA SPLIT	Netter	6.2	1.85	37	1997	F	GBR
p	PZ80	ANN ROSA	Liner	5.1	0.94	22	1996	F	GBR
p	SN34	BOLD VENTURE	Potter	5.91	1	22	1990	F	GBR

FH200 Jen-Lou - 12/03/2013

FH293 Girl Pauline - 12/03/2013

Ex FH340 Tamalin - 24/02/2007

FH468 Girl Jan - 06/10/2010

LO540 Banana Split - 14/04/2008

FH613 (Ex M613) **Kerany** - 12/03/2013

Ex PZ80 Ann Rosa - 06/10/2010

SN34 Bold Venture - 14/04/2008

COVERACK

The Harbour looking South East

The Harbour looking NE towards The Manacles

Coverack, which gets its name from being a 'Hidden Place' has a small drying out harbour, protected by a breakwater that was built in 1724.   Much of Coverack's history centres round smuggling and wrecking, but there is no doubt that it has also had a thriving fishing history founded like many Cornish ports on the pilchard fishing. One of the old salting cellars is now a gift shop overlooking the harbour. The Spanish Armada was first sighted from the cliffs close to Coverack. The fleet has nearly doubled since 2006 and about 15 small fishing vessels, - potters, netters and liners - now operate from the attractive harbour, some of them by part time fishermen.   In the winter, due to the port's exposure to easterly gales, most of them are pulled high up the slipway beside the old lifeboat house, but a few operate year round.   In the summer the boats are sometimes moored offshore as the harbour dries out completely at low water. In early 2013 Coverack received a grant of £100,000 which will be used to replace the winch which dates from 1900, and is used to haul the boats out of the water, a new quayside hoist, and a new cold store with ice maker. The lifeboat was withdrawn in 1972 after 70 years service, but an inshore lifeboat remained until 1985. The nearby 'Paris Hotel' gets its name from the stranding of the liner 'SS Paris' on the nearby menacing 'Manacles' rocks in 1899.

Returning from Boat moored offshore

COVERACK FISHING VESSELS

P	PLN	VESSEL NAME	Type	LOA Mtrs	Gross Tons	Eng Kw	Year Built	Hull	Nat Build
p	BK524	KINDLY LIGHT D	Liner	7.45	2.84	60	1990	F	GBR
p	FH1	SULA	Potter/Liner	6.1	2	11	1951	W	GBR
p	FH11	SEA FOAM	Potter	7.38	2.65	22	1955	W	GBR
p	FH19	LADY MARGARET	Liner	4.9	1.1	147	2010	F	GBR
p	FH57	FOXY LADY	Netter	4.74	1.25	13	1990	F	GBR
p	FH71	SOUTHERN STAR	Netter/Liner	4.74	1.04	13.4	1990	F	GBR
p	FH106	FLYING BREEZE	Netter/Liner	6.19	1.98	13	1967	W	GBR
p	FH280	EVENING STAR	Netter/Potter	6.25	2.66	38	1973	W	GBR
p	FH494	SON-A-MOR	Potter/Liner	6.16	2.65	14	1979	F	GBR
	FH699	SUNSHINE	Liner	3.66	0.38	3		F	
p	FH717	CORNISH LASS IV	Potter	4.89	1.1	6.71	2003	F	GBR
p	FH744	MINSTREL	Netter/Liner	4.64	1.1	6.71	2003	F	GBR
p	FH746	MILLY II	Netter/Potter/Liner	5.96	2	10	1986	F	GBR
p	Ex PZ44	AMY ROSE	De-registered	4.75	1.24	7	1985	F	
p	PZ477	MARY ROSE	Potter/Liner	5.6	1.77	9	1987	F	GBR
p	PZ771	SILENUS	Netter	6.5	3.13	28	1969	F	GBR

BK524 Kindly Light D - 12/03/2013

FH1 Sula - 12/03/2012

FH11 Sea Foam - 09/07/2012

FH19 Lady Margaret - 09/07/2012

FH57 Foxy Lady - 09/07/2012

FH71 Southern Star - 09/07/2012

FH106 Flying Breeze - 06/10/2010

FH280 Evening Star - 14/04/2008

FH494 Son-a-Mor - 22/11/2005

FH717 Cornish Lass IV - 09/07/2012

FH744 MINSTREL - 09/07/2012

FH746 Milly II - 09/07/2012

Ex PZ44 Amy Rose - 13/04/2007

PZ477 Mary Rose - 06/10/2010

PZ771 Silenus - 12/03/2012

Cadgwith landing beach from the Todden

The Todden

Cadgwith is a beautiful fishing village with delightful thatched cottages nestling in a valley within a sheltered bay on the east side of the Lizard. The bay is split in two by a rocky outcrop called 'The Todden'. At the height of the pilchard fishing era a record daily catch of 1,300,000 fish was landed. The watch station on the cliffs to the north of the bay is considered by some to be an old 'Huers' Hut, but the locals maintain that it has only been a watch station used by the coastguards. In the 19th century a steam engine on 'The Todden' outcrop operated an overhead cable across the bay to offload visiting colliers. A fleet of eight medium sized fishing vessels operates from the port, potting and netting, including some seine netting for pilchards, but in the winter mainly potting with up to 500 pots per boat. The catches are refrigerated locally, and taken on a regular basis by road to the fish market in Newlyn. Most of the vessels are Falmouth (FH) registered. Some newer boats have replaced older boats using the same name and PLN. It is quite impressive to see the boats returning and literally driving up onto the shingle beach. The 'Razorbill 'featured in the recent BBC programme 'The Fisherman's Apprentice'. A cooperative scheme to sell fish locally after the programme has yet to gain momentum.

Huer's Hut??

Fleet 'Line up'

CADGWITH FISHING VESSELS

P	PLN	VESSEL NAME	Type	LOA Mtrs	Gross Tons	Eng Kw	Year Built	Hull	Nat Build
p	Ex FH324	SILVER QUEEN	De-registered	7.16	4.09	36	1977	F	GBR
p	FH324	SILVER QUEEN	Netter/Potter	7.46	2.6	41	2009	F	GBR
p	FH414	STARLIGHT	Netter/Potter	7.62	3.84	41	1977	F	GBR
p	Ex FH529	KINGFISHER II	De-registered	7.77	4.24	41	1981	F	GBR
p	FH529	KINGFISHER II	Netter/Potter	7.62	2.72	46	2010	F	GBR
p	FH691	BOB WINNIE	Netter/Potter	5.8	2.13	31	1999	F	GBR
p	FH706	VICTORIA ANN	Netter	5.9	1.24	37.3	2002	F	GBR
p	PZ601	FULMAR	Potter	5.85	1.47	12	2002	F	GBR
p	PZ707	SCORPIO	Netter/Potter	7.75	2.27	51.3	1996	F	GBR
p	SS268	RAZORBILL	Netter	5.6	1.51	11	1979	F	GBR

Ex FH324 Silver Queen - 13/04/2007

FH324 Silver Queen - 06/10/2010

FH414 Starlight - 05/11/2004

Ex FH529 Kingfisher II - 25/05/2005

FH529 Kingfisher II - 12/03/2012

FH691 Bob Winnie - 13/04/2007

FH706 Victoria Ann - 13/04/2007

PZ601 Fulmar - 06/10/2010

PZ707 Scorpio - 13/04/2007   **SS268 Razorbill** - 06/10/2010

SS268 - The Fisherman's Apprentice

21 CHURCH COVE

The Cove's Steep Slipway   **Very exposed to the east**

On the eastern side of the Lizard is the attractive small bay of Church Cove. Fishing craft no longer operate from here on a regular basis. A lifeboat operated from Church Cove for five years from 1885 to 1889, and a very modern new lifeboat house was completed in late 2011 at the adjacent Kilcobben Cove to replace that built on the same site in 1961.

(This Church Cove is not to be confused with Gunwalloe Church Cove (by the parish Church of St Winwalloe) at the eastern tip of Mounts Bay. The name 'Fishing Cove' was given to the shingle beach area nearby, because fishing was carried out from it but this has now died out. It is said that the buccaneer James Emery buried large quantities of treasure on that beach and a ship carrying a cargo of silver dollars was wrecked near here in the 17th century at a place locally known as 'Dollar Cove'. Several well organised attempts have been made to recover any of the treasure but although several coins have indeed been found there has been little profitable to reward these efforts. However if you feel like some digging exercise perhaps you will be lucky, but not if you identify the wrong Church Cove!)

The Disused Lifeboat Station   **The Lizard slipway**

On the West side of the Lizard itself, but almost on the tip is Polpeor Cove. It contains the old 1914 lifeboat station which was abandoned in 1961 since it was often too rough to launch into the south westerly seas and gales. The new lifeboat station was built at Kilcobben Cove - just west of Church Cove. Polpeor Cove is where the Cornish Choughs were first re-established nesting on the Cornish mainland. Three 'Toshers' still operate from the slipway beside the old lifeboat house. During the winter months these boats may be seen up the Helford River, or at Newlyn or Mullion Cove.

THE LIZARD FISHING VESSELS

P	PLN	VESSEL NAME	Type	LOA Mtrs	Gross Tons	Eng Kw	Year Built	Hull	Nat Build
p	FH93	IDA MAY	Netter	4.5	0.9	6	1990	F	GBR
p	FH629	KATHRYN LOUISE II	Netter	4.5	0.84	3	1985	F	GBR
p	FH731	TIDOS	To Clovelly	5.55	1.4	10	1972	F	GBR
p	PZ79	JOSH II	Potter/Liner	5.55	1.13	7	1980	F	GBR

FH93 Ida May 27/05/2006   **FH629 Kathryn Louise II** - 06/10/2010

FH731 Tidos - 13/04/2007   **PZ79 Josh II** - 05/04/2013

Mullion Cove (looking South West)　　　　　**Mullion Slipway**

Although exposed to the prevailing south westerlies, Mullion Cove gets some protection from an offshore island. Early in the 19th century a thriving pilchard seining industry grew up with five seine companies, but this collapsed in the late 19th century when the shoaling pilchard numbers reduced. The fish cellars by the slipway can still be seen. The harbour piers were built between 1870 and 1895 by Lord Robartes of Lanhydrock to support the fisherman, who adapted to potting after the shoals of pilchards repeatedly failed. Despite some changes there are still three small fishing vessels operating from the port.

MULLION COVE FISHING VESSELS

Photo	PLN	VESSEL NAME	Type	LOA Mtrs	Reg Tons	Eng Kw	Year Built	Hull	Nat Build
p	PZ453	LAURIE JEAN	Potter	5.6	4.22	84	1966	W	GBR
p	PZ574	FLOWING TIDE　(Ex M574)	Potter	5.55	1.74	7	1977	F	
p	PZ1200	CELTIC SUNRISE	Netter	5.94	1.76	15	-	F	
p	Ex SA28	ROBBYN　(Now WY839)	To Scarborough	5.06	1.3	9.8	1995	F	GBR

PZ453 Laurie Jean - 05/04/2013

PZ574 (Ex M574) **Flowing Tide** - 05/04/2013

PZ1200 Celtic Sunrise - 05/04/2013

Ex SA28 Robbyn - 06/10/2010

PORTHLEVEN

Inner Harbour looking North

Outer Harbour (Entrance in distance)

A fishing hamlet was established at Porthleven in the 14th century. The port was subsequently developed, mainly to support the mining industry, as well as being a haven for the fishing industry. The outer harbour was completed in 1825 using POW (Prisoner of War) labour from the Napoleonic Wars. Unusually in harbour construction, the inner harbour came at the later date of 1855, with timber baulks used to block the entrance from the outer harbour in heavy weather. As a commercial port it was never a success however. Huge shoals of pilchards used to enter Mounts Bay every summer, and in the late 19th century Porthleven supported a fleet of up to 144 vessels. Most were involved in drift netting, rather than the usual seine netting in the area. A record catch of 2000 hogsheads was recorded in November 1884 *(One hogshead = 2,500-3000 fish in a 54 gallon barrel)*. About twenty small vessels still operate from the port, mainly netters, potters and liners with crab, lobster and crayfish being the main catches, most of which are taken to nearby Newlyn for marketing. The number of active boats has increased from about 15 boats in 2006 to 18 in 2013. The harbour is still rather exposed in winter gales especially as the entrance faces the prevailing South Westerly winds, and the sight of seas crashing over the outer harbour wall in winter can not only be very impressive, but very dangerous. In December of 1978 two policemen drowned when their police car was swept into the harbour from the harbour road *(See plaque below left)*. The building of wooden fishing vessels in Porthleven only stopped in about 1970.

The Eastern Breakwater

Entering The Inner Harbour

In Memoriam

The Harbour Entrance

PORTHLEVEN FISHING VESSELS

P	PLN	VESSEL NAME	Type	LOA	Reg	Eng	Year	Hull	Build
				Mtrs	Tons	Kw	Built		Nat
p	BM511	MAGNUM	Liner	5.8	1.6	5	1992	F	GBR
p	FH243	ST RUAN	Netter	9.9	8.1	100	1976	F	GBR
p	FH735	SWEET TART	Not Registered	5.16			2012	A	
p	FY167	CORAL REEF	Netter	5.7	1.9	7	1951	W	GBR
p	NN95	CHRISANN	Netter	4.90	1.1	7	1980	F	GBR
p	PZ9	MORNING STAR (Ex PZ21)	Netter	7.67	4.32	30	1989	W	GBR
p	PZ18	KATY	Liner	4.89	1	7	2005	F	GBR
	PZ21	LADY OF ENNIS		5.86	1.23	22.4	2012	F	GBR
p	PZ26	MAGLER-MOR	Liner	6.27	2.2	10	1970	W	GBR
p	PZ50	ENNIS LADY	To Scarborough	7.3	3.57	64	2004	F	GBR
p	PZ64	ST ELVAN	Potter/Liner	4.8	1.4	10	1980	F	GBR
p	Ex PZ68	STARFISH	De-registered	9.6	8.8	64	1942	W	GBR
p	PZ76	RHIANNON	Netter/Potter	6.2	1.8	10	2007	F	GBR
p	PZ76	SHEILA T	To be registered	8.5		59.5	1980	F	GBR
p	PZ95	BOY CODY	Liner	5.6	1.5	12	1992	W	GBR
p	PZ127	OSPREY (Ex WK127)	Netter/Potter	9.9	6.4	184	1987	F	GBR
p	PZ260	OUR KATIE	Netter	7.0	3.6	20	1962	W	GBR
p	Ex PZ402	SEA SPRAY	De-registered	5.56	1.4	25	1977	F	GBR
p	Ex PZ475	RELIANCE	De-registered	9.3	6.8	75	1965	W	GBR
p	PZ609	DANDA	Potter	8.2	4.4	53	1978	W	GBR
p	PZ677	SALAMANDA	Potter	6.9	2.7	11	1985	F	GBR
p	PZ1197	BOY JAMES	Liner	5.38	1.4	6	1989	F	GBR
p	PZ1198	GOLDEN FLEECE	Potter	5.8	2.5	22	2000	G	GBR
p	SS258	TUDOR ROSE	Liner	5.5	1.2	7	1988	F	GBR

Note: On going to print PZ76 'Sheila T' was about to replace PZ76 'Rhiannon'

BM511 Magnum - 19/04/2013   **FH243 St Ruan** - 20/01/2013

Ex FH735 Sweet Tart - 20/01/2013

FY167 Coral Reef - 09/07/2012

NN95 Chrissan - 13/04/2007

PZ9 Morning Star - 06/10/2010

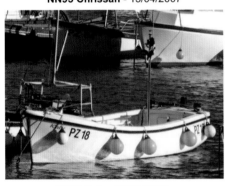

PZ18 Katy - 06/10/2010

PZ26 Magler-Mor - 03/06/2009

PZ50 Ennis Lady - 24/08/2007

PZ64 St Elvan - 01/04/2008

Ex PZ68 Starfish - 06/10/2010

PZ76 Sheila T - 20/01/2013

PZ76 Rhiannon - 13/04/2007

PZ95 Boy Cody - 29/08/2009

PZ127 (Ex WK127) **Osprey** - 20/01/2013

PZ260 Our Katie - 06/10/2010

Ex PZ402 Sea Spray - 24/08/2007

PZ609 Danda - 06/10/2010

PZ677 Salamander - 29/08/2009

PZ1197 Boy James - 06/10/2010

PZ1198 Golden Fleece - 21/10/2010

SS258 Tudor Rose - 09/07/2012

Entrance to the Inner harbour

Inner harbour baulked off

Porthleven sea defences

St Michael's Mt looking North (Note Causeway)   **Marazion's small Harbour 'Top Tieb'**

Marazion is almost certainly the oldest port in Cornwall, and it is believed that tin was exported from here as early as 2000BC. The Romans also used it in the 1st century AD. The beach at Marazion is however very exposed and a harbour was gradually developed on the north side of St Michaels Mount which both provided superb shelter and an excellent defensive position. The first record of a harbour dates back to 1320 when there were short harbour walls. It was developed as a major port in 1470 and remained as such until the development of Penzance in the 17th century. This explains why it is such a large harbour for what seems a relatively small population now. At about that time a French raiding party landed and failed to take the Mount but razed Marazion to the ground. For all its good shelter the island harbour is fairly shallow and dries out at low water, so it rapidly lost trade when Penzance developed with its far superior communications especially when the railways arrived in the South West. During the 19th century at the height of the pilchard boom it was one of the many fishing ports with fish curing cellars. Most of these have been destroyed but the building on the left at the entrance from the causeway is the oldest building in the village and was one of the old fish cellars and now used as a general store. The restaurant was also one of the old fish cellars. Marazion itself has just a very small harbour called 'Top Tieb', which is used as a ferry port when the entire causeway is covered by the high tide. At half tide the ferry uses the steps on 'Chapel Island', which is connected to the mainland by a slightly higher stretch of the causeway. The causeway itself can be used two hours either side of low water. It was built in 1898 on top of the natural shingle bank. The one registered fishing vessel (PZ4) that was based in St Michael's harbour, was sold to an owner in Hartlepool but it returned to Newlyn in 2012. It was owned by one of the castle watermen who are known locally as 'Hobblers', and was appropriately named *'Cormoran'* after the mythological giant who 'founded' the island. The Mount was gifted to the National Trust in the 1950s.

Harbour - Marazion in distance

Aerial view of Penzance Harbour

Penzance got its name in 1284 from 'Penn Sans' which translated from the Cornish means Holy Headland. The Haven dates back to 1327, and it was a major fishing port. In 1512 there was a small pier or quay but no harbour. Like Mousehole and Newlyn it was ransacked by the Spanish in 1595, but it was recorded as having fully recovered by 1612. In the 17th century it was developed and took over from Marazion which until then was the major port in the area. By 1800 it had became the major export harbour in the far South West for the produce of both the tin mining, and the herring and mackerel fishing industries. Fish for the London markets were transported by sea to Portsmouth and onward by road. Exports went as far as Russia and Italy. The 'Old Pier' which forms the southern wall to what is now the floating harbour was built in 1766, and extended in 1785 and 1812. The inner harbour, which dries out, was fully enclosed by the construction of the Albert Pier on the north side in 1853. Part of it has now been filled in to form the main Penzance car park. The still operational dry dock on the west side was originally built in 1814, but rebuilt in 1880. Access is via the inner harbour and through the Ross Swing Bridge into 'Abbey Basin'. The railway arrived, thanks to Brunel, in 1852, and the Ross Bridge was built in 1881 to provide access from the railway station to the main harbour, and subsequently replaced 100 years later in 1981. The Central pier enclosing the floating harbour with a lock gate allowing access 2 hours either side of high water was built in 1884. The fish market came later. Penzance's importance as a fishing port has declined as Newlyn has expanded, and since the new pontoons were completed in Newlyn in 2006 most of the boats have moved over to Newlyn, but many return to Penzance for maintenance. Many of the heritage sailing vessels are based in Penzance harbour. Most fishing vessels from the west side of The Lizard to the Land's End Peninsula bear the Penzance (PZ) registration. The original 'PE' for Penzance was transferred to Poole in 1869. The ferry service to the Isles of Scilly operates from the inside of the breakwater just outside the lock gate. There is a total lack of storage space for goods awaiting or off loading the ferry and there has been much talk of upgrading the ferry terminal facilities, which would mean changing the immediate coastline south of the port.

Environmentalists oppose this and there has been talk of moving the ferry to Falmouth if improvements are denied. Now that the helicopter service to St Mary's and Tresco from Penzance has closed as well, this could be a disaster for the town.

The old Custom House was between the port and the church and probably not as indicated in Custom House Street.

Penzance Dry Dock

Lock Gate into the Floating Dock

Ross Bridge, Lighthouse & St Michael's Mt
(White building is the Old Fish Market)

PENZANCE FISHING VESSELS

Photo	PLN	VESSEL NAME	Type	LOA	REG	Eng	Year	Hull	Nat
				Mtrs	Tons	KW	Built		Build
p	Ex PH82	NEPTUNE (Ex Pt Wrinkle)	De-registered	4.4	0.8	3	1996	W	GBR
p	PZ88	VIKING (Charters)	Angler	9.62	4.3	127	1995	F	GBR
p	Ex PZ545	SARAH ANN	De-registered	4.88	1.4	5	1980	F	GBR
p	Ex PZ824	BOY GABRIEL	De-registered	7.92.2	2.3		2000	F	GBR

Ex PH82 Neptune - 29/08/2009

PZ88 Viking - 09/07/2012

Ex PZ545 Sarah Ann - 03/07/2007

Ex PZ824 Boy Gabriel - 03/01/2011

Ross bridge, Harbour Entrance & Dry Dock Gate into the Abbey Basin on right

This definitely was the custom House on left, and probably was not on the right!

The two floating pontoon piers - (Middle right and behind Old breakwater on Left)

To the memory of Bill Best Harris 1914-1987 Historian and son of Plymouth whose researches indicated that the MAYFLOWER 16-8-1620 docked at the Old Quay Newlyn for water and supplies making it the last port of call in England The water supply at Plymouth being the cause of fever and cholera in the city
Let debate begin

Newlyn dates back to about 1300, and like Penzance and Mousehole it was also ransacked by the Spanish in 1595. It was the final departure point for the Pilgrim Fathers on the Mayflower in 1620. Having left Plymouth they were forced in because the drinking water picked up in Plymouth was foul. The original small harbour can be seen in the south east of the current harbour and small fishing craft still use it. Despite this small and somewhat shallow harbour Newlyn gradually developed into a major fishing port, and in the late 19th century it supported several seines, mackerel and herring fisheries, with the largest drifter fleet in the South West of 130 vessels. After Penzance had fully enclosed its harbour by construction of the Northern Albert Pier in 1847, many of Newlyn's fishing fleet used to seek shelter in Penzance's safer harbour in the advent of bad weather. However, after several vessels were lost crossing the bay whilst seeking shelter, it was decided to enlarge Newlyn's facilities. The short South Pier was completed in January 1887 and the North Pier two years later but extended to its present length in 1894. A cast iron lighthouse on the South Pier was erected in 1887, but when the pier was extended by 90 feet in 1914, a new similar lighthouse was built. The fishing industry really expanded after the central Mary Williams Pier was built in 1988. Although there are now many visiting boats from all over the country and abroad they have not always been well received. In 1896 serious rioting occurred when the fishermen of Newlyn tried to prevent East Coast fishermen landing their catches, particularly on Mondays after weekend fishing. The Methodist Newlyn fishermen, on strict Christian principles, never fished on Sundays, and resented this 'unholy' competition. Until October 2005, Newlyn boasted the last remaining fish cellar where fish where salted and packed in wooden casks using the traditional methods for the European market. Sadly that tradition has now died, although packing has continued using more modern methods. Newlyn, like most ports operating the larger fishing vessels is suffering from the huge recent fuel price rises, making the operation of the older, and less fuel efficient, larger boats no longer profitable. It was also hit hard in 2007/9 by the results of two court cases involving the owners of six of the port's large netters and some of the boats operated by the main Newlyn

The restored Lugger SS19 'Ripple' in the old harbour

company W S Stevenson.   These resulted in heavy fines.   Reduction of fleet numbers and downsizing of boats was inevitable. Only three of the six boats survived the financial crisis, one of which later sank in 2011. Stevenson has also reduced their fleet of some 30 trawlers by almost half in the last 10 years. Somewhat surprisingly, the total number of boats operating out of Newlyn has actually increased, from about 145 boats in 2006 to about 183 in 2013. The size and tonnage of the boats has decreased quite significantly though, and the number of vessels of length greater than 20 metres has dropped from 55 to 26 and over 10 metres from 66 to 53. Most of the additions to the ports numbers are boats of less than 8 metres in length and are primarily used for line fishing. The fish caught by this method are more popular with the customers as they are less damaged than those caught using either netting or trawling. The numbers of boats used for line fishing out of Newlyn has more than doubled from 33 to 75. The two new pontoon floating piers completed in 2006 *(See below)* now provide most of these smaller craft with individual pontoon berths, and my favourite view of the line up of

toshers shown here can no longer be seen. An-other change has been the introduction of ring netters. One or two boats have been converted for ring netting, while there are a few brand new boats designed specifically for this. Newlyn is still one of the largest fishing ports in the UK with about 183 boats of all types and sizes. In terms of tonnage and value of catch landed, it was the largest fish producing port in England until 2004, but it has since been overtaken by Brixham. Newlyn's £10m fish market, completed in 2005, has followed Plymouth in introducing auctioning for the fish catches 'on line' which has proved very successful.   Most of the catches are sold for export.
Set into the quayside on the North Pier is a plaque showing the magnetic variation of 18° 50' West in

Variation Plaque

1897. Variation changes by about 1° East in 8 years and at present it is only 2° West so it is interesting to see how much it has changed in 115 years, and how much more important it was at that time. The lugger 'Mystery' sailed from Newlyn to Melbourne with a crew of eight to 'Search for Gold' in a 4 month passage from 18th November 1854 to 14th March 1855. On 20th October 2008 Peter Goss sailed a replica lugger the 'Spirit of Mystery' over the same route arriving in Melbourne on 9th March 2009. The 'Mystery' was similar to the 1896 lugger 'Ripple' (SS19) which was relaunched in Newlyn on 12th October 2007 after restoration *(See Pages 87 & 116)*.

The Old Drying Out Harbour (North Pier and Lighthouse beyond)

The pontoon moorings installed in 2006

NEWLYN FISHING VESSELS

P	PLN	VESSEL NAME	Type	LOA Mtrs	Reg Tons	Eng Kw	Year Built	Hull	Nat Build
p	Ex BD57	JACAMAR	To Campbelltown	8.57	3.1	180	1999	F	GBR
p	BF7	TRANQUILITY	To Fraserburgh	20.6	54.34	399	1988	S	GBR
p	BM35	SHIRALEE	Trawler	9.8	12.9	143	1979	W	
p	Ex BM298	GEORGE JOHANNES	De-registered	26.24	122.0	507	1969	S	NLD
p	Ex DH42	SAINT PETROX	Decommissioned 2009	7.77	3.5	68	1978	F	GBR
p	Ex FH14	JASPER	To Plymouth	5.42	1.05	26	2003	F	GBR
	FH18	BEST EVER	Liner	5.92	1.49	56	2008	F	GBR
	FH30	AUTUMN ROSE		6.55	1.9	39	2002	F	GBR
p	FH32	BESS	Liner	6.46	1.71	28	1989	F	GBR
	FH35	DOROTHY ANN		6.45	1.54	73.6	2011	F	PRT
p	FH49	TREGLOWN (Ex PZ49)	Potter/Liner	7.87	2.3	60	1987	F	GBR
p	Ex FH121	BRITANNIA V	De-registered	15.45	47.3	289	1986	W	GBR
p	FH145	COPIOUS (Ex FY37)	Twin Rig Trawler	13.99	28.9	200	1990	S	GBR
p	FH401	GOLDEN PROMISE (Ex FR186)	Scalloper	14.2	35.4	179	1996	S	GBR
p	Ex FH508	BRITANNIA IV of FALMOUTH	De-registered	10	10.95	95	1980	W	GBR
p	FH610	SEA LASS (Ex SC1)	Liner	5.85	0.9	45	2003	F	GBR
p	Ex FH614	BOY DANIEL	De-registered	4.40	6.46	120	1996	F	GBR
p	FH623	BENEDICTION	Netter/Potter	5.85	2	22	1993	F	GBR
p	FH704	RUBEN LUKE	Netter/Liner	6.08	1	37	2002	F	GBR
p	FH750	MYGHAL	Netter/Potter	8.47	8.4	134	2008	F	GBR
p	FY11	TORRI GWYNT (Ex M11)	Liner	4.8	1.4	15	1990	F	GBR
p	FY23	LITTLE PEARL	Netter	9.98	12.9	130	1997	F	GBR
p	FY46	INNISFALLEN	Trawler	10.00	10.0	118	1986	W	GBR
p	FY83	ELISABETH VERONIQUE(Ex B974)	Trawler	14.98	36	171	1984	S	GBR
p	FY119	RESOLUTE	Ring Netter	9.95	11.4	104	2004	F	GBR
p	FY570	SILVERY SEA	Netter	9.6	8.8	73	1980	W	GBR
p	FY765	LITTLE ANNE	Liner	4.88	1.09	7	1992	F	GBR
p	Ex FY781	LINDA B	To Scarborough as PW10	6.70	2.35	10	1986	W	GBR
p	Ex FY824	GIRL BRYHER	Decommissioned 2009	5.80	2.1	19	1999	F	GBR
p	GY356	PANDION	Trawler	9.15	5.76	64	1987	S	GBR
p	HL257	ACHIEVE	To North Shields	9.93	14.6	126	1997	F	GBR
p	Ex KY144	BLUE FIN	De-registered	6.18				F	GBR
p	LT61	SEA SPRAY	Netter	9.93	11.4	120	1988	F	GBR
p	P1007	KASTEL PAOL	Potter	17.4	38.8	167	1978	W	FRA
p	PL26	CHRIS TACHA	Potter	16.2	102	214	1987	S	GBR
p	PW3	SPARKLING LINE (Ex GY364)	Netter	17.3	39.43	231		S	GBS
p	Ex PW12	NANTEWAS	De-registered	9.93	11.2	129	1987	S	GBR
p	PW33	DIANA MARION	Liner	6.5	1.2	26	1984	F	GBR
p	PW156	SERENE DAWN (Ex OB156)	Netter	11.86	27.5	189	1989	F	GBR
p	PW177	HARVEST REAPER (Ex TT177)	Netter	17	78	191	1975	W	GBR
p	PW346	SEA STAR	Liner	5.60	0.9	48	1981	F	GBR
p	PW473	VIDDY	Netter	4.91	0.3	6	1991	F	GBR
p	PW479	ANN KATHLEEN	Potter	8.2	4.5	140	2002	F	
p	PZ1	SARAH BETH	Netter/Potter	8.76	6.2	63	1985	F	GBR
p	PZ4	CORMORAN	Netter	6.19	2.9	37	1999	F	GBR

p	PZ5	SOU'WESTER	Liner	5.48	1.4	11	1990	F	GBR
p	PZ6	GIRL PAMELA	Netter	11.48	12.6	94	1968		GBR
p	PZ7	PORTHENYS	Liner	5.6	1.1	17	1976	F	GBR
p	PZ10	KAREN N (Ex Nellie)	Scalloper	22.18	126	220	1988	S	GBR
p	PZ11	BOY DYLAN	Liner	5.8	1.27	29.4	1985	F	GBR
p	PZ12	STEREN MOR	Liner	7.52	2	60	1994	F	GBR
p	Ex PZ14	SOWENNA	To Cork	17.98	44.6	367	1989	F	GBR
p	PZ15	CAPRIOLE	Angler	10.35	3.9	194	1989	F	
p	Ex PZ19	J-ANNE (Ex BRD92)	Decommissioned 2009	8.93	6.6	134	1982	F	GBR
	PZ20	JENNY		4.69	1.0	8	1980	F	GBR
p	PZ22	SARAH - M	Liner	5.91	2.6	13	1980	F	GBR
p	PZ23	TREEN	Liner	4.86	0.8	5	2000	F	GBR
p	Ex PZ24	BOY DANNY	De-registered	6.5	2.5	64	2006	F	GBR
p	PZ32	CATHRYN	Trawler	12.16	17.3	85	1955	W	GBR
p	PZ35	KARENZA (Ex SC170)	Netter/Potter	6.16	2.5	37	2002	F	GBR
p	Ex PZ41	OCEAN SPRAY	De-registered	14.11	26.1	205	1990	W	GBR
p	PZ47	LOWENA - MOR	Netter/Potter/Liner	6.0	2.2	15	1986	F	GBR
p	PZ56	CORNISH ROSE	Liner	5.5	1.1	50	2007	F	GBR
p	Ex PZ57	GIRL PATRICIA	SANK 28/05/2008	17.80	84.0	240	1969	U	GBR
p	PZ61	GUIDING STAR	Liner	5.5	1.5	63		F	GBR
p	PZ62	SEA FOX	Netter/Liner	5.87	2.1	22	1991	F	GBR
p	PZ63	GOLDEN HARVEST	Netter	15.02	24.8	134	1972	F	UNK
p	PZ66	SAPPHIRE	Beam Trawler	25.05	91.0	369	1958	S	NLD
p	Ex PZ67	DAB	De-registered	5.65	1.5	25	1980	F	GBR
p	PZ69	EMMA ROSE	Liner	7.47	4.2	15	1967	W	GBR
p	PZ70	TRISTY	Liner	5.85	1.9	19	1989	F	GBR
p	Ex PZ72	LAURAN	De-registered	4.76	1.3	7	1992	F	GBR
p	PZ75	WILLIAM HARVEY	To Dartmouth	12.64	15.6	97	1958	W	FRA
p	PZ78	JAMES R.H. STEVENSON	Beam Trawler	29.80	153.0	559	1969	S	NLD
p	PZ81	LYONESSE	Ring Netter	12	18.1	348	2008	F	GBR
p	PZ82	CHICADEE	Tender	7.01	2.5	59	1935	W	GBR
p	PZ83	LOUELLA	Liner	4.45	0.6	7	1973	F	GBR
p	PZ85	GIRL KIM	Potter	6.03	1.64	8	1968	W	GBR
p	PZ86	KATHLEEN	Potter	6.05	2	10	1979	F	GBR
p	PZ90	ATLANTIC BELLE	Liner	5.8	1.2	41	1999	F	GBR
p	PZ92	EVENING STAR	Liner	5.9	1.5	13	1991	F	GBR
p	PZ97	WORTH LASS	Liner	6.15	1.6	20	1982	F	GBR
p	PZ98	LEADER	Netter/Potter	5.5	1.3	7	1914	W	GBR
p	PZ100	ELIZABETH N	Beam Trawler	22.52	100.0	220	1984	S	NLD
p	PZ101	LOUISA N (Ex BM28 Angel Emiel)	Beam Trawler	23.1	125	219	1990	S	POL
p	Ex PZ110	IMOGEN II (Ex KY202)	To Mallaig	13.08	20.69	216	1981	S	GBS
p	PZ110	IMOGEN II (Ex OB15)	Trawler	11.95	23.78	127	1990	F	GBR
p	PZ111	JOSEPHINE	Liner	5.6	1	22		F	GBR
p	PZ115	SAPPHIRE II	Beam Trawler	26.5		986	1991	S	NLD
p	PZ118	PENDOWER	Liner	5.6	1.56	7	1992	F	GBR
p	Ex PZ123	SARA SHAUN	De-registered	25.32	127.0	373	1960	S	GBR
p	PZ137	TWILIGHT III	Beam Trawler	29.10	141.0	783	1969	S	NLD
p	PZ166	VENTURE	To Brixham	5.49	1.6	7	1946	W	GBR

p	PZ182	ASTHORE	Ring Netter	14	23	223	2011	F	GBR
p	Ex PZ184	CERES	De-registered	6.70	2.5	10	1956	W	GBR
p	PZ187	NOVA SPERO (Ex CN187)	Tuna Liner/Netter	20.43	110	317	1973	W	GBR
p	PZ191	WILLIAM S STEVENSON	Beam Trawler	28.24	142.0	611	1969	S	NLD
p	PZ193	TREVESSA 1V	Beam Trawler	26.15	135.0	611	1969	S	NLD
p	PZ195	WILLIAM STEVENSON	Beam Trawler	25.99	104.0	560	1967	S	NLD
p	PZ198	AALTJE ADRIAANTJE	Beam Trawler	28.60	125.0	492	1967	S	NLD
p	PZ199	ALGRIE	Beam Trawler	26.20	121.0	525	1968	S	NLD
p	Ex PZ203	A B S	De-registered	25.28	126.0	369	1960	S	GBR
p	PZ218	SPRIGS OF HEATHER	Liner	5.58	1.7	7	1975	F	GBR
p	PZ272	WHITE HEATHER	Liner	5.61	1.59	8	1973	F	GBR
p	PZ291	MY LASS (Ex RX330)	Netter	9.1	5.3	56	1977	F	GBR
p	Ex PZ293	ELIZABETH CAROLINE	Scrapped 2012	29.85	143.0	373	1946	W	GBR
p	Ex PZ295	MARIE CLAIRE	De-registered	29.85	157.0	492	1946	W	GBR
p	PZ302	BOY ADAM	Netter/Liner	5.86	2	22	1992	F	GBR
p	PZ307	JACOBA (Ex UK307)	Beam Trawler	37	418	754	1975	S	NLD
p	PZ315	TAMSIN T	Liner	5.51	1.6	14		F	GBR
p	PZ329	HARVEST REAPER	Trawler	11.88	21.8	173	1988	S	GBR
p	Ex PZ331	ANTHONY STEVENSON	De-registered	23.33	78.0	238	1945	W	GBR
p	PZ336	NAZARENE (Ex SS700 Highlander)	Netter/Liner	8.36	5.2	95	2001	F	GBR
p	PZ339	CORNISH LASS	Tender	7.98	4.2	90	1950	W	GBR
p	PZ395	LISA	Tender	6.74	2.5	33	1960	W	GBR
p	PZ410	SEA HUNTER	Netter	5.20	1.2	22	1981	F	GBR
p	PZ425	CKS	Netter	16.73	42.7	171	1973	W	GBR
p	Ex PZ436	L'AURORE (Ex Michael & David	Now CM2369	11.09	8.4	83	1954	W	FRA
p	PZ437	FRANCES ROSE	Netter/Liner	5.56	1.6	15	1994	F	GBR
p	PZ439	ELLEN (Ex Lugi)	Liner	4.5	0.8	7		F	GBR
p	PZ476	LISA JACQUIE STEVENSON	Beam Trawler	24.20	112.0	447	1973	S	NLD
p	Ex PZ481	VIPA	De-registered	5.6	1.7	19	1974	F	GBR
p	PZ481	VIPA	Liner	6.3	2.9	213	1992	F	GBR
p	PZ498	STELLISA	Netter	20.6		270	1991	S	FRA
	PZ499	TWILIGHT		8.02	4.3	26	1969	F	GBR
p	PZ512	CORNISHMAN	Beam Trawler	32.82	208.2	671	1971	S	NLD
p	Ex PZ513	EXCELLENT	De-registered	24.75	75.0	208	1931	W	GBR
p	PZ527	BASS BOY	Liner	5.14	1.1	6	1981	F	GBR
p	PZ532	BILLY ROWNEY	Beam Trawler	31.86	187.0	706	1973	S	NLD
p	PZ542	FILADELFIA	Beam Trawler	26.26	131.0	611	1969	S	DNK
p	Ex PZ550	PRUE ESTHER II	Now CY550@Stornaway	11.60	13.3	373	1987	F	GBR
p	PZ592	ALICE LOUISE	Netter/Liner	7.94	3.4	61	1978	F	GBR
p	PZ611	NIK-NAK	Liner	5.62	1	7	1977	F	GBR
p	PZ612	RACHEL & PAUL	Netter/Liner	5.6	1.7	7	1980	F	GBR
	PZ638	RO-MI-CHRIS		4.88	1.0	7	1979	F	GBR
p	PZ641	MARK & JAMES	Liner	5.5	1.8	7	1979	F	GBR
p	PZ643	GARY-M	Netter	11.87	21.2	175	1982	W	GBR
p	Ex PZ645	BEN MY CHREE	SANK 12/03/2011	17.25	29.4	214	1965	W	GBR
p	PZ663	CYNTHIA	Liner	5.6	1.55	7	1980	F	GBR
p	PZ689	JOHN LOUISE	Liner	4.76	1.5	13	1980	F	GBR

p	PZ715	CARES LEL		Liner	5.60	1.5	13	1979	F	GBR
p	PZ718	THREE BOYS		Liner	5.04	1.0	11	1978	F	GBR
p	PZ729	PEGASUS		Potter	6.42	3.0	22	1981	F	GBR
p	PZ738	OUR MARGARET		To North Shields	5.57	1.9	11	1948	F	GBR
p	PZ768	ONWARD		Liner	4.73	1.3	13	1989	F	GBR
p	PZ775	OCEAN BREEZE		Liner	5.62	1.7	15	1991	F	GBR
p	PZ778	NAOMI G		Liner	4	0.56	11.0	1992	F	GBR
p	Ex PZ779	JACK-ANNY		De-registered	4.68	1.2	5	1988	F	
p	Ex PZ787	HOUR OFF		De-registered	6.75	1.9	100	2005	F	GBR
p	PZ800	REBECCA ANNE		Liner	5.58	0.6	12	1991	F	GBR
p	Ex PZ810	ALVIC		De-registered	5.64	1.8	15	0	F	
p	PZ815	BARRACUDA		Liner	5.60	0.5	18	1985	F	GBR
p	Ex PZ818	JAY JAY		Not registered					F	
p	PZ826	TUPPENCE		Liner	5.54	1.4	8	1990	F	GBR
p	PZ828	ANGELS		To Gt Yarmouth	7.90	2.2	50	2009	F	GBR
p	Ex PZ888	UTSKER		De-registered	9.95	7.8	108	1998	A	NOR
p	Ex PZ890	LITTLE WATERS		De-registered	11.28	11.1	112	1978	F	GBR
p	PZ903	GO-FOR-IT		Netter/Liner	7.30	2.9	57	1998	G	GBR
p	Ex PZ999	JANNIE EN KLAAS		De-registered	26.15	108.0	462	1969	S	NLD
p	PZ1001	RESURGAM		Beam Trawler	26.22	134.0	447	1969	S	NLD
p	Ex PZ1024	ROS-NA-RIOGH		Private yacht	14.45	24.5	125	1953	W	GBR
p	PZ1053	ST GEORGES		Beam Trawler	34.78	237.0	820	1973	S	NLD
p	PZ1184	CLAIRVOYANT	(Ex M126)	Netter	8.96	4.12	60	1974	W	GBR
p	Ex PZ1186	CHLOE T	(Ex BM190)	SANK 2 Sep 2012	26.24	136.0	313	1968	S	NLD
p	PZ1193	ELLIE MAE		Netter/Potter	6.70	3.4	30		G	GBR
p	PZ1196	SILVER DAWN		Netter	17.93	118.0	171	2001	S	GBR
p	Ex PZ1212	TWO BOYS		De-commissioned 2009	9.99	5.5	80		W	UNK
p	PZ1218	SARAH STEVE		Potter/Angler	8.01	3.8	170	2005	F	GBR
p	Ex PZ1225	FREEDOM		De-registered	5.52	2.10	37.0	2000	F	POL
	PZ1228	TRENOW GIRL		Liner	4.50	0.6	6	2005	F	GBR
p	PZ1247	LADY JACQUELINE		Liner	6.75	1.8	59	2007	F	PRT
p	SC1	TORRIBEE	(Ex FH610)	Liner	5.85	0.9	454	2003	F	GBR
p	SC2	LOWENA		Potter/Liner	6.90	29.80	37	2008	F	GBR
	SC5	SUMMERTIME BLUES			6.8	2.57	17	2007	F	GBR
p	SC7	HAPPY HOOKER (Ex Piscatio II)		Liner	6.9	1.15	74.6	2005	F	GBR
p	SC8	DANMARK	(Ex M8)	Trawler	9.77	8.42	112	1979	S	GBR
p	SC14	STAR of the NORTH	(Ex UL4)	Netter/Potter	8.49	4.2	60	1974	W	GBR
p	SC21	NAZARENE		Liner	4.8	1.1	15	1989	F	GBR
p	SC25	NORTHWOOD		Liner	7.47	2.3	41	1990	F	GBR
p	SC50	ZEPHYR		Liner	5.84	2.3	22	1984	F	GBR
p	Ex SC178	LOWENDA		De-registered	9.98	4.05	93	2006	F	GBR
p	SC181	SOWENNA		Netter	7.85	4.90	170	2009	F	GBR
p	Ex SC183	RETARRIER		De-registered	8.45	3.79	44	1988	F	GBR
p	SD201	NEPTUNE		Trawler/Scalloper	9.95	11.8	199	1991	S	GBR
p	SS19	RIPPLE		Lugger	13.4	18.18	75	1896	W	GBR
p	SS21	TIGER		Liner	5.6	1.43	15	1974	F	GBR
p	SS22	INSPIRATION		Liner	5.60	1.5	17	1966	W	GBR
p	SS28	LAMORNA		Netter	12.0	14.6	94	1986	W	GBR

p	SS30	ROSEBUD	(Ex Scilly)	Liner	4.72	0.50	6	1980	F	GBR
p	SS33	WHITE HEATHER	(Ex LK3390)	Netter	12.4	26.4	179	1988	F	GBR
p	SS65	HOPE		Liner	6.05	1.26	30	2010	F	GBR
p	SS76	TILLERMAN		Liner	5.85	2.1	25	1988	F	GBR
p	SS87	PRIDE OF CORNWALL		Ring Netter	9.9	8	118	2005	S	GBR
p	SS92	ELISHIA		Netter/Liner	5.6	1.7	7	1975	F	GBR
p	Ex SS94	GIRL YASMIN		De-registered	4.7	1.0	4	1985	W	GBR
p	SS118	CRYSTAL SEA		Twin Rig Trawler	20.94	158	399	1989	W	FRA
p	SS126	NIKKI LOUISE		Netter	6.25	1.15		1923	W	GBR
p	SS136	CYNTHIA		Liner	5.59	1.7	11	1974	F	GBR
p	SS138	PETER PAN		Liner	5.7	2.2	7	1977	F	GBR
p	SS144	JANET ANNE		Netter	5.6	1.4	7	1977	F	GBR
p	SS252	BETHSHAN		Liner	7.98	5.1	90	2010	F	GBR
p	SS276	BOY CHRIS		Liner	4.74	1.2	5	1978	F	GBR
p	SS717	BOY DANIEL		Liner	5.5	1.7		1979	F	GBR
	SS723	SIR JACK			4.8	0.8	27	2002	F	PRT
p	SS739	AUTUMN SILVER		Liner	5.97	1.50	13		F	GBR
p	SS748	RAVEN	(Ex M748)	Liner	4.77	1.1	15	2007	F	GBR
p	ST5	DREAM CATCHER		Liner	5.4	1.4	26	1990	F	GBR
p	Ex TH148	TRITON		De-registered	7.50	6.5	52	1979	F	GBR
p	TN35	OLIVIA JEAN	(Ex BM181)	Beam Trawler	33.86	242	749	1980	S	NLD
p	TO5	MARINA II		Liner	7.27	4.9	54	1986	F	GBR
p	TO32	AJAX	(Ex AH32)	Netter	16.98	74.0	238	1972	W	GBR
p	TO40	INTUITION		Potter	17.98	53.3	176	1995	F	GBR
p	TO41	BOY RYAN		Liner	4.78	0.9	7		F	GBR
p	TO50	EMMA LOUISE	(EX PZ203 ABS)	Crabber	25.28	126.0	369	1960	S	GBR
p	Ex TO50	CESCA	(Ex FR1 Accord)	Now M99 @ Neyland	16.46	23.2	179	1968	W	GBR
p	TO60	EMMA LOUISE		Potter	16.42	106	164	2012	S	GBR
p	Ex TO60	DOM-BOSCO	(Ex PW78)	De-registered	17.22	24	214	1959	W	FRA
p	Ex TO61	HAPPY HOOKER (Ex P Delicia)		De-registered	6.28	1.8	45	2003	F	GBR
p	WH97	DRAGUM-AN-MOAR		Liner	6.6	3.6	27	1982	F	GBR
p	WH264	PROSPECTOR		Potter	9.89	7.0	101	1974	F	GBR
p	WH578	BOY BRAX (Ex AMRO)		Netter/Liner	5.6	1.8	9	1980	F	
p	Ex WH367	HANNAH KATE		To Swansea	8.1	3.3	149	1988	F	GBR
p	WK3	BEN LOYAL		Tuna Liner	21.22	66.0	171	1960	W	UNK
p	WY160	LEON		Potter	9.55	6.0	120	1987	W	GBR
p	Ex WY379	CAROL H		De-registered	18.71	69.0	235	1975	S	GBR

Cornwall's Fisheries Patrol Vessel 'St Piran' based at Newlyn

Ex BD57 Jacamr - 26/03/2007

BH9 Valhalla - 08/03/2010

BM35 Shiralee - 31/03/2009

Ex BM298 George Johannes - 01/04/2008

Ex DH42 Saint Petrox - 03/07/2007

Ex FH14 Jasper - 03/10/2012

FH32 Bess - 19/02/2012

FH49 (Ex PZ49) Treglown - 22/09/2012

Ex FH121 Britannia V - 12/04/2010

FH145 (Ex FY37) Copious - 10/04/2010

FH401 (Ex FR186) Golden Promise - 03/01/2011

Ex FH508 Britannia IV of Falmouth-19/02/2012

FH610 (Ex SC1) Torribee - 03/01/2011

Ex FH614 Boy Daniel - 12/04/2010

FH623 Benediction - 09/07/2012

FH704 Ruben Luke - 31/07/2009

FH734 Patricia Anne - 14/03/2010

FH750 Myghal - 13/01/2012

FY11 Torri-Gwynt - 22/09/2012

FY23 Little Pearl -19/02/2012

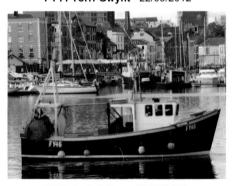

FY46 Innisfallen - 22/10/2010

FY83 (Ex B974) **Elisabeth Veronique** - 12/04/2010

FY119 Resolute - 25/01/2010

FY570 Silvery Sea - 13/01/2012

FY765 Little Anne - 03/01/2011

Ex FY781 Linda B - 04/07/2008

Ex FY824 Girl Bryher - 26/06/2008 (DL)

GY356 Pandion - 05/04/2013

Ex HH76 Osprey - 13/02/2007

HL125 Bonny Lass - 31/03/2009

HL257 Achieve - 23/06/2008 (DL)

Ex KY144 Blue Fin - 03/09/2011

LT61 Sea Spray - 11/08/2006

P1007 Kastel Paol - 20/01/2013

PL26 Chris Tacha - 20/01/2013

PW3 Sparkling Line - 03/09/2011

Ex PW12 Nantewas - 03/07/2008

PW33 Diana Marion - 09/07/2012

PW156 Serene Dawn - 20/01/2013

PW177 (Ex TT177) **Harvest Reaper** - 03/01/2011

PW346 Sea Star - 03/06/2009

PW473 Viddy - 02/03/2009

PW479 Ann Kathleen - 19/09/2012

PZ1 Sarah Beth - 02/07/2010

PZ4 Cormoran - 05/04/2013

PZ5 Sou'wester - 05/04/20113

PZ6 Girl Pamela – 11/08/2006

PZ7 Porthenys - 03/07/2008

99

PZ10 Nellie - 03/09/2011

PZ11 Boy Dyllan - 20/01/2013

PZ12 Steren Mor - 03/09/2011

Ex PZ14 Sowenna - 15/07/2008

PZ15 Capriole - 02/03/2009

PZ16 Spitfire - 03/01/2011

Ex PZ19 (Ex BRD92) **Jacqueline Anne** - 02/03/2009

PZ22 Sarah-M - 12/04/2010

PZ23 Treen - 13/01/2012

Ex PZ24 Boy Danny - 13/02/2007

PZ32 Cathryn - 05/04/2013

PZ35 Karenza (Ex SC170) - 12/04/2010

Ex PZ41 Ocean Spray - 13/01/2012

PZ47 Lowena-Mor - 03/01/2011

PZ56 Cornish Rose - 01/04/2008

Ex PZ57 Girl Patricia - 19/06/2006

PZ61 Guiding Star - 09/07/2012

PZ62 Sea Fox - 02/07/2010

PZ63 Golden Harvest - 05/04/2013

PZ66 Sapphire - 31/07/2009

Ex PZ67 Dab - 01/04/2008

PZ69 Emma Rose - 25/01/2010

PZ70 Tristy - 09/07/2012

Ex PZ72 Lauran - 12/04/2010

PZ75 William Harvey - 15/07/2008

PZ78 James R HStevenson - 13/01/2012

PZ81 Lyonesse - 15/07/2008

PZ82 Chicadee - 05/04/2013

PZ83 Louella - 12/04/2010

PZ85 Girl Kim - 01/04/2008

PZ86 Kathleen – 13/01/2012

PZ90 Atlantic Belle - 09/07/2012

PZ92 Evening Star - 05/04/2013

PZ97 Worthy Lass -12/04/2010

PZ98 Leader - 03/06/2009

PZ100 Elizabeth N - 17/12/2008

PZ101(Ex BM28) **Louisa N** - 05/04/2013

Ex PZ110 (Ex KY202) **Imogen II** - 03/09/2011

PZ110 (Ex OB15) **Imogen II** - 05/04/2013

PZ111 Josephine - 21/10/2008

PZ115 Sapphire II - 20/01/2013

PZ118 Pendower - 20/01/2013

Ex PZ123 Sara Shaun - 06/10/2007

PZ137 Twilight - 02/03/2009

PZ166 Venture - 03/01/2011

PZ182 Asthore - 19/02/2012

Ex PZ184 Ceres - 12/04/2010

PZ187 (Ex CN187) **Nova Spero** - 09/07/2012

PZ191 William S Stevenson - 02/03/2009

PZ193 Trevessa IV - 09/10/2008

PZ195 William Stevenson - 02/03/2009

PZ198 Aaltje Adriaantje - 01/04/2008

PZ199 Algrie - 21/10/2008

Ex PZ203 A B S - 23/06/2008 (DL)

PZ218 Sprigs of Heather - 02/03/2009

PZ272 White Heather - 13/01/2012

106

PZ291 (Ex RX330) **My Lass** - 19/02/2012

Ex PZ293 Elizabeth Caroline - 13/01/2012

Ex PZ295 Marie Claire - 02/03/2009

PZ302 Boy Adam - 15/07/2008

PZ307 Jacoba - 03/09/2010

PZ315 Tamsin T - 11/08/2006

PZ329 Harvest Reaper - 13/02/2007

PZ336 (Ex SS700) **Nazarene** - 05/04/2013

PZ339 Cornish Lass - 04/07/2008

PZ395 Lisa - 02/03/2009

PZ410 Sea Hunter - 20/01/2013

PZ425 C K S - 13/01/2012

Ex PZ436 L'Aurore Ex Michael & David - 29/09/2009

PZ437 Frances Rose - 31/07/2009

PZ439 Ellen (Ex Lugi) - 03/06/2009

PZ476 Lisa Jacquie Stevenson - 20/11/2011

Ex PZ481 Vipa - 12/04/2010

PZ481 Vipa - 19/02/2012

PZ498 Stelissa - 20/01/2013

PZ512 Cornishman - 19/02/2012

Ex PZ513 Excellent - 29/08/2009

PZ527 Bass Boy - 03/01/2011

PZ532 Billy Rowney - 29/08/2009

PZ542 Filadelfia - 29/08/2009

Ex PZ550 Prue Esther II - 14/10/2008

PZ592 Alice Louise - 03/07/2007

PZ611 Nik-Nak - 29/08/2009

Ex PZ611 Tan-Nos - 20/01/2013

PZ612 Rachel & Paul - 20/01/2013

PZ641 Mark & James - 11/07/2008

PZ643 Gary-M - 20/01/2013

Ex PZ645 Ben My Chree - 12/04/2010

PZ663 Cynthia - 09/07/2012

PZ689 John Louise - 20/01/2013

PZ715 Cares Lel - 03/01/2011

PZ718 Three Boys - 03/09/2011

PZ729 Pegasus - 03/07/2008

PZ738 Our Margaret - 29/09/2009

PZ768 Onward - 12/04/2010

PZ775 Ocean Breeze - 19/02/2012

PZ778 Naomi G - 26/03/2007

Ex PZ779 Jack-Anny - 12/04/2010

PZ787 Hour Off - 13/01/2012

PZ800 Rebecca Ann - 13/02/2007

Ex PZ810 Alvic - 22/09/2012

PZ815 Barracuda - 03/01/2011

Ex PZ818 Jay-Jay - 12/04/2010

PZ826 Tuppence - 09/07/2012

PZ828 Angels - 03/01/2011

PZ882 Sea Lion - 12/10/2010

Ex PZ888 Utsker - 07/03/2007

PZ890 Little Waters - 03/07/2008

PZ903 Go-For-It - 29/08/2009

Ex PZ999 Jannie en Klaas 03/07/2008

PZ1001 Resurgam - 03/09/2011

Ex PZ1024 Ros-Na-Riogh - 15/07/2008

PZ1053 St Georges - 29/08/2008

PZ1184 (Ex M126) **Clairvoyant** - 22/09/2012

Ex PZ1186 Chloe T - 06/10/2007

PZ1193 Ellie Mae - 17/03/2007

PZ1196 Silver Dawn - 03/09/2011

Ex PZ1212 Two Boys - 13/02/2007

PZ1218 Sarah Steve - 24/08/2007

Ex PZ1225 Freedom - 29/09/2009

PZ1247 Lady Jacqueline - 03/06/2009

SC1 (Ex FH610) **Sea Lass** - 22/09/2012

SC2 Lowena - 08/07/2008

SC7 Happy Hooker - 05/04/2013

SC8 (Ex M8) **Danmark** - 20/01/2013

SC14 (ExUL4) **Star of the North** - 05/04/2013

SC21 Nazarene - 13/01/2012

SC25 Northwood - 21/09/2012

SC50 Zephyr - 03/09/2011

SC178 Lowenda - 16/11/2006

SC181 Sowenna - 19/02/2012

Ex SC183 Retarrier - 13/01/2012

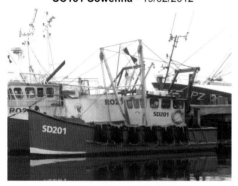

SD201 Neptune - 03/09/2011

SS19 Ripple - 03/09/2011

SS21 Tiger - 20/01/2013

SS22 Inspiration - 14/10/2008

SS28 Lamorna - 03/01/2012

SS30 Rosebud - 04/07/2008

SS33 White Heather - 09/07/2012

SS65 Hope - 05/04/2013

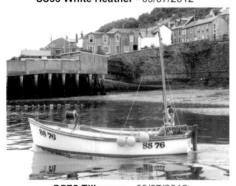

SS76 Tillerman - 09/07/2012

SS87 Pride of Cornwall - 05/05/2013

SS92 Elishia - 26/04/2005

SS118 Crystal Sea - 02/11/2011

SS126 Nikki Louise - 02/03/2009

SS136 Nikki Louise - 27/12/2005

SS138 Peter Pan - 29/09/2009

SS144 Janet Anne - 05/04/2013

SS252 Bethshan - 03/09/2011

SS276 Boy Chris - 09/07/2012

SS717 Boy Daniel - 09/07/2012

SS739 Autumn Silver - 03/09/2011

SS748 (Ex M748) **Raven** - 22/09/2012

ST5 Dream Catcher - 03/09/2011

Ex TH148 Triton - 01/04/2008

TO5 Marina II - 03/03/2011

TO32 (Ex AH32) **Ajax** - 19/02/2012

TO40 Intuition - 03/09/2011

TO41 Boy Ryan - 03/01/2011

Ex TO50 (Ex PZ203) **Emma Louise** - 03/09/2011

Ex TO60 Dom-Bosco - 03/07/2008

TO60 Emma Louise - 20/01/2013

Ex TO61 Happy Hooker - 09/07/2012

WH97 Dragun-An-Moar - 03/09/2011

WH264 Prospector - 09/07/2012

Ex WH367 Hannah Kate - 29/09/2009

WH578 Boy Brax - 03/09/2011

WK3 Ben Loyal - 03/06/2009

Ex WY160 Leon - 22/09/2012

Ex WY379 Carol H - 02/03/2009

A reminder of the days when Newlyn was busier!

One half scrapped!!

North Pier

Old Harbour

Mary Williams Pier

South Pier

Aerial View of Newlyn Harbour (Before pontoon moorings installed)

Mousehole Harbour and Village

Inner Harbour looking North

Mousehole, pronounced 'Mowzull', was the original major port for the extreme South West and part of the south 'Great Quay' dates back to 1390 when it was the first harbour to have a pier in Cornwall. It was originally called 'Porthenys' which means 'Cove island' due to the rocky St Clement's Island which provides some protection to the port. There was a small chapel recorded on the island in 1540, though there is some dispute over whether a chapel ever existed there. It was renamed Mousehole in the 13th century possibly because of a nearby deep cave. Records show cured pilchards and pilchard oil were exported to France as early as 1302, and it remained the most important fishing harbour in Cornwall until Penzance was developed in the 16th Century. A Spanish raiding party of some 400 men ransacked and virtually destroyed it in 1595 before going on to attempt the same at Newlyn and Penzance. Mousehole never really recovered. By 1750 there were 70 boats recorded at Newlyn which was about twice the number at Mousehole. The 'Great Quay' was extended and the harbour enclosed in 1838 by a pier from the shore straight out to the current harbour entrance. This enclosed area quickly proved to be too small, so this pier was destroyed and the stone used to build the current north 'New Pier' in 1870. Even then the

St Clement's Island off the Entrance

harbour was too small for the numbers of craft using it. It played an important part in the Cornish pilchard and mackerel fishing era, but mainly with drifters rather than seining, and employing about 800 people. There are still several netters, liners and potters based here, taking advantage of the reduction in the time taken to get the catch round to Newlyn after fishing off Lands End. It is in the lee of the prevailing south westerly winds, and although the St Clement's Island rock provides some protection from a south easterly wind, it still suffers in a strong south easterly gale with the waves breaking over the harbour wall, and from early November to late March the harbour entrance is baulked off with timbers. Many of the Mousehole boats then operate from Newlyn itself. Its semi-circular shape and unspoilt cottages make it one of the most attractive harbours in the South West, with the boats' mooring lines radiating in towards the harbour entrance.

In Mousehole a sign commemorates the last monoglot speaker of Cornish (Kernewek), but this is disputed as an old Fisherman *(as he described himself)* claimed also to speak the language in 1776 when he was aged 65 years. He outlived Dolly by 11 years - but there could have been others living into the 19th century. By the time the language was almost dying out measures were taken to revive it with Cornish language classes and today there are estimated to be around 3-400 fluent Cornish language speakers, and possibly around 2,000 with some conversational potential. Bilingual English/Cornish road signs are appearing in many areas. The speaking of the Cornish language as the prime language was more prevalent in the Penwith areas of Cornwall.

HERE LIVED
DOLLY PENTREATH
ONE OF THE LAST
SPEAKERS OF THE
CORNISH LANGUAGE
AS HER NATIVE TONGUE
DIED DEC. 1777

Plaque in Mousehole

MOUSEHOLE FISHING VESSELS

Photo	PLN	VESSEL NAME	Type	LOA	Reg	Eng	Year	Hull	Nat
				Mtrs	Tons	KW	Built		Build
p	CN119	ISLANDER	Netter	6.21	2.3	21	1988	F	GBR
p	PW453	DOO DA DAY	To Sheerness	7.1	1.5	67	1999	F	GBR
p	Ex PZ11	BOY DYLAN	De-registered	5.8	1.3	29	1985	F	GBR
p	Ex PZ21	PANDORA III	De-registered	4.50	0.7	3	2005	F	GBR
p	PZ91	CLAIR	Liner	4.33	0.79	7	1969	F	GBR
p	PZ94	TARA ROSE	Liner	4.29	0.6	8	2010	F	GBR
p	PZ457	LILY	To Mallaig	5.00	1.4	5	1974	W	
p	PZ580	AQUILA	Netter/Potter/Liner	4.8	1.2	9	1978	F	GBR
p	PZ584	BUTTS	Netter/Liner	5.73	1.4	13	1977	F	GBR
p	Ex PZ758	LITTLE HALCYON	De-registered	4.60	0.9	4	1970	F	GBR
p	PZ816	ROSE of MOUSEHOLE	Liner	5.6	1.5	8	1990	F	GBR
p	PZ1199	SEA GOBLIN	Liner	4.85	0.71	10.1	2002	F	GBR
p	SC19	FORGET-ME-NOT	Netter	6.35	3.1	22	1981	F	GBR
p	SS151	HAWK	Liner	5.60	2.0	8		F	
p	SS273	ORION	Netter/Liner	8	3.9	22	1978	F	GBR
p	SS694	MIDGE	Liner	5.55	1.4	24	1985	F	GBR
p	Ex SS718	EEL-AVUM	De-registered	5.18	1	15	1980	F	GBR

CN119 Islander - 16/11/2006

Ex PW453 Doo-Da-Day - 12/04/2010

Ex PZ11 Boy Dylan - 29/09/2009

Ex PZ21 Pandora III - 12/04/2010

PZ91 Clair - 12/04/2010

PZ94 Tara Rose - 09/07/2012

PZ457 Lily - 03/06/2009

PZ580 Aquila - 31/07/2009

PZ584 Butts - 06/10/2007

PZ816 Rose of Mousehole - 05/04/2013

PZ1199 Sea Goblin - 05/04/2013

SC19 Forget-Me-Not - 04/07/2008

SS151 Hawk - 03/09/2011

SS273 Orion - 22/09/2012

SS694 Midge - 09/07/2012

Ex SS718 Eel-Avum - 06/07/2007

St Michaels Mount
through Harbour
Entrance

29 LAMORNA COVE

Lamorna Cove is three miles South West of Mousehole. It is a small fishing hamlet within a small rocky bay although there is some sand at low tide. The harbour was used for the export of granite stone from the nearby now disused quarries. Many of the Mousehole buildings were constructed from Lamorna granite. The small quay is protected by a short harbour breakwater and wall which has suffered considerable storm damage. The cost of restoration cannot be justified and the harbour is being left to nature. There are no longer any fishing vessels operating from this cove. There are splendid views from the nearby coastal walk but the path itself is rocky.

PENBERTH

The Slipway

The 'Big Cellar' (Central building)

Penberth is a intriguing small cove near Lands End from which up to eight small hand liners and potters operate. The old capstan winch, dating from pre1840, has been beautifully restored by the National Trust. It was used to haul the boats up from the beach, but now the electric winches are used. The fish cellar called the 'Big Cellar' was constructed in the mid 19th Century, and remains of the old pilchard presses can still be seen. A tar boiler was installed about 100 years later, while a more recent addition is an ice making machine installed in 2005. The stone clapper bridge and the ancient masonry (using natural rounded stones) diverting the stream around the slipway are beautiful in their simplicity and the slipway, made from rounded stones from the beach and smoothed down by years of use, is again fascinating. The hand lining is for both bass and mackerel in season.

Stone Clapper Bridge to the Beach

Restored Windlass

Beautiful smooth
stoned slipway

PENBERTH FISHING VESSELS

Photo	PLN	VESSEL NAME	Type	LOA	Reg	Eng	Year	Hull	Nat
				Mtrs	Tons	KW	Built		Build
p	PZ39	FATHER BOB	Liner	4.6	1.3	16	1990	F	GBR
	PZ53	SUNRISE	Liner	4.4	0.8	3	1972	F	GBR
p	Ex PZ151	(Not Known)	De-registered						
p	PZ536	GAZELLE	Liner	4.7	1.1	6	1978	F	GBR
p	PZ540	GREY SEAL	Liner	4.6	1.3	15	1977	F	GBR
p	PZ585	CURLEW	Liner	4.78	1.29	13	1991	F	GBR
p	PZ620	CAROL & DAVID	Liner	4.8	1.0	7	1978	F	GBR
p	PZ631	PENVER	Liner	4.6	1.3	15	1978		
p	PZ654	HICCA	Liner	4.8	1.1	7	1988	F	GBR

PZ39 Father Bob - 03/01/2011

Ex PZ151 (Name unknown) - 26/04/2005

127

PZ536 Gazelle - 24/01/2005

PZ540 Grey Seal - 03/01/2011

PZ585 Curlew - 26/04/2005

PZ620 Carol & David - 03/01/2011

PZ631 Penver - 24/01/2005

PZ654 Hicca - 24/01/2005

Line up on the beach

The Boat Winch, Storage Chambers & Slipway

Porthgwarra is another fascinating historic fishing cove, but the one fishing vessel that was here no longer operates . There is a steep slipway to the sea made from the sea rounded stones, and a tunnel through to the beach from the hamlet. This was built by Cornish Miners to allow wagons access to the beach to pick up sea weed for fertilizer. Another tunnel also dug out by the miners connects the beach to where live fish storage chambers used to exist cut into the rocks. The National Coastwatch station monitoring marine traffic round Land's End is just west of the harbour at Gwennap Head.

NCI Station At Gwennap Head

Tunnel from Slipway to Fish Storage Traps

Wagon Tunnel down to Slipway

PORTHGWARRA FISHING VESSEL

Photo	PLN	VESSEL NAME	Type	LOA	Reg	Eng	Year	Hull	Nat
				Mtrs	Tons	Kw	Built		Build
p	Ex PZ25	WHITE ROSE	De-registered	4.6	0.8	7	1990	F	GBR

PZ25 White Rose - 29/05/2005

Sennen Cove looking North

Capstan House Centre – Lifeboat Station Right

Circular Capstan Room

Sennen took the name Sennen from the Cornish word Senne for Pilchard, and, as the name suggests, it is another small harbour that was developed because of the Pilchards. It is naturally quite well protected by Land's End itself and Cape Cornwall to the North, and the short breakwater extending northwards was built in 1908, but the weather stops much activity in winter. The boats are winched up the beach, and the old circular capstan room which was built in 1876 is now a shop. The capstan and machinery were recovered from one of the local mines when it ceased working. As well as pilchards, shoals of mullet often appeared in the bay during the month of March which the Sennen Covers jealously considered was there for them and them only. Even today on the rare occasions when the right weather, sea state and fish shoals combine the 'Senners' resort to the old method of 'Beach Seining' for mullet by using a rowing boat from the shore to encircle the shoals with a seine net and haul them in to the beach. Up to ten 'Toshers' operate from the Cove - potting, lining and netting. The lifeboat station has been in service since 1853 and is unusual in having two slipways - one for launch, and one for recovery.

Working Views of Sennen

SENNEN COVE FISHING VESSELS

Photo	PLN	VESSEL NAME	Type	LOA	Reg	Eng	Year	Hull	Nat
				Mtrs	Tons	Kw	Built		Build
p	PZ124	REMY-D	Liner	5.12	1.2	6	1995	F	GBR
p	PZ155	SARAH JANE T	Liner	4.6	0.6	14	1996	F	GBR
p	PZ490	BARRY ANN	Potter	5.0	1.0	11	1989	F	GBR
p	PZ564	TAMARA	Netter/Potter	4.5	0.8	7	1977	F	GBR
p	PZ699	BOY MATT	Netter	4.9	1.3	7	1967	F	GBR
p	PZ747	PENNY LYNN	Liner	5.6	1.7	11	1982	F	GBR
p	PZ770	POL PRY II	Netter	4.8	0.9	7	1989	F	GBR
p	PZ1209	ROSE BUD	Potter/Liner	4.86	1.2	10	2003	F	GBR
p	SS7	DIANA	Liner	4.9	0.9	4	1979	F	GBR
p	SS226	DAPHNE ROSE	Liner	4.8	1.1	5	1977	F	GBR

PZ124 Remy-D - 11/07/2008

PZ155 Sarah Jane T - 31/07/2009

PZ490 Barry Ann - 31/07/2009

PZ564 Tamara - 03/01/2011

Sennen Launch

Tow down the beach and Push into the water

PZ699 Boy Matt - 04/07/2008

PZ747 Penny Lynn - 31/07/2009

PZ770 Pol Pry II - 03/01/2011

PZ1209 Rose Bud - 24/08/2007

SS7 Diana - 03/01/2011

SS226 Daphne Rose - 03/01/2011

View looking South towards Land's End   **'Toshers' on the Slipway**

Almost opposite Sennen Cove to the north is Cape Cornwall and nestling in the shelter of the Cape is Priest's Cove, from which small craft have fished for at least 150 years. Only three registered colourful 'Toshers' are now engaged in netting, potting and line fishing for crabs, lobster and mackerel. The beach consisting of sand and shingle gradually eroded away and the concrete slipway was built in 1960, to ease landings on the remaining rocky shore line. It is surrounded by fishermen's huts made by the men themselves from beach stones and wreckage washed ashore, and is now all in the protection of the National Trust. The winter seas can be very dangerous and fishing only takes place in the summer. There is a splendid view of Land's End, and further out to the Isles of Scilly.

Slipway and Fishermen's Huts

CAPE CORNWALL FISHING VESSELS

Photo	PLN	VESSEL NAME	Type	LOA	Reg	Eng	Year	Hull	Nat
				Mtrs	Tons	KW	Built		Build
p	PZ84	PEN KERNOW	Liner	4.5	0.8	7	1973	F	
p	PZ146	ANNA CATHERINE	Potter	4.4	0.8	5	1978	F	GBR
p	PZ478	LYONESSE of CAPE	Liner	4.4	0.8	7	1970	F	GBR
p	Ex PZ570	RACHEL CARA	De-registered	4.5	0.75	7	1977	F	GBR
p	Ex PZ777	GLORIA	De-registered	4.4	0.8	11		F	GBR

PZ84 Pen Kernow - 19/09/2012

PZ146 Anna Catherine - 17/04/2006

PZ478 Lyoness of Cape - 24/01/2005

Ex PZ570 Rachael Cara - 19/09/2012

Fishermen's Huts

Ex PZ777 Gloria - 19/09/2012

BOAT COVE

Boat Cove slipways   'Toshers' on the Slipway

In the lee of Pendeen Point with its prominent lighthouse is a small hidden cove. It has been an active fishing cove since the late 16th century and was in use before Newlyn started. Although sheltered from the prevailing SWly winds it is rather exposed to a NEly wind. The steep concrete slipway was constructed in 1860 and the proceeds of the first catch after that were sufficient to pay for a prominent house nearer the lighthouse with a cellar beneath it for processing the mackerel There was another storage cellar beside the slipway. A powerful Petter engine hauls the boats up the main slipway out of the sea and there is another steep slipway up to a level area from which wagons and vehicles could take the catch to market. This was constructed in 1960 with an asymmetric trolley which could ride up the slope with a horizontal loading platform. The boat hauling wire was cleverly passed via the rocks to the top of the slope so that it could be used to haul the trolley up the slope. A natural spring feeds a basin beside the slipways for cleaning both boats and catches. Three small toshers are based here used for line catching mackerel. In 2012 there were few mackerel caught which was blamed on much larger vessels catching them in huge numbers further out to sea.

A retired fisherman after 40 years fishing from the cove now lives overlooking it in a smart cabin with only candlelight and a wireless for company.

Pendeen Lighthouse

Approach to the Cove facing North East

Fisherman's Huts with the Cove and Portheras Beach beyond

BOAT COVE FISHING VESSELS

Photo	PLN	VESSEL NAME	Type	LOA	Reg	Eng	Year	Hull	Nat
				Mtrs	Tons	KW	Built		Build
p	PZ2	J.S.W	Liner	4.45	0.68	7	1996	F	GBR
p	PZ343	RUBY MAE	Liner	4.88	0.52	7	1964	F	NOR
p	SS9	CADOR	Liner	4.4	0.46	7	1978	F	GBR

PZ2 J.S.W - 19/09/2012

PZ343 Ruby Mae - 19/09/2012

SS9 Cador - 19/09/2012

Hauling wire for unloading trolley

Spring Water

Looking West into St Ives Harbour   **Along Smeaton's Pier – West Pier beyond**

St Ives is one of the oldest fishing harbours in Cornwall and was the major Cornish fishing port in the Middle Ages. In the 16th century it was one of the main departure points for Ireland. A short eastern pier was built during the 15th century to provide some shelter, and it was rebuilt in 1770 by the well known engineer - John Smeaton. A short pier out to the north was built in 1815 and extended in 1864 but the sea destroyed most of it by 1880. An extension to Smeaton's East Pier was later completed in 1890, angled further out to the east and with a new cast iron light house. By the late 18th century and early 19th century the port had developed as the major pilchard fishery in Cornwall with three quarters of the county's 379 'Seines', and nearly a third of the county's registered drift netters. With so many Seines operating the order of priority when the shoals were sighted, had to be decided at the start of the season by a racing match between seine crews. Rules of operation for Seines were laid down in the mid 17th century. The old 'Huer's' hut *(for some reason called the 'Baulking House')* is sited on Porthminster Point, due south of the town overlooking St Ives Bay towards Godrevy Lighthouse, and judging by the covered bench seating either side of it, seining was a popular spectator sport!! It is accessible on the coast path, but sadly not open to the public. At its peak the St Ives Fishery landed up to 22 million pilchards per year, and some of these were exported directly to Italy. The last major seine 'enclosure' was in August 1916 and seining ended in 1920. Some copper and tin ores were exported through St Ives to South Wales from the nearby mining area of St Just, and the West Pier *(near the church)* was built in 1894 to export stone from quarries nearby, but St Ives was predominantly a fishing port. At the landward end of Smeaton's Pier is the old Fishermen's Chapel dedicated to St Leonard. On the wall of the chapel is a commemoration of the 1902 passage of a St Ives lugger from Scarborough to St Ives in 50 hours!! About thirty small fishing craft still operate from the port, netting, potting and lining. Many of these boats spend considerable time in Newlyn, depending on the weather and where the fish are to be found. Similarly about thirty of the Newlyn smaller craft will be found in St Ives in the summer, and since some of the Hayle boats will often be seen at St Ives as well, one will often see many more boats in the harbour than are actually based in St Ives.

SAINT LEONARD'S CHAPEL
The traditional chapel of the fishermen of St. Ives

Remains of north pier

The 'Baulking House' Huer's Hut

THE BAULKING HOUSE
A Huer's Lookout from which watch was kept for shoals of pilchards in the bay and the movements of the seine boats were directed

Sign on the Huer's Hut

ST IVES FISHING VESSELS

P	PLN	VESSEL NAME	Type	LOA Mtrs	Reg Tons	Eng Kw	Year Built	Hull	Nat Build
p	FH506	SILVER LANCE	Netter	5.6	1.8	22	1980	F	GBR
p	FY47	OUR LIZ	Netter	8.7	5.2	66	1963	W	GBR
p	DH47	AUTUMN SILVER ll (Ex M&SS747)	To Dartmouth	5.5	1.1	30	1994	F	GBR
p	M1103	HELEN D	To Fishguard	5.9	2	12	2000	F	GBR
p	Ex PZ3	WE-RE HERE	De-registered	3.17	0.4	4	1980	F	GBR
p	PZ40	GEMMA	Netter/Liner	6.5	3.0	35	1979	F	GBR
p	PZ43	DAISY MAE (Ex ENIGMA)	To Milford	5.9	2.3	13	1981	F	GBR
p	PZ49	ATHENA-FAY	Liner	6	1.3	27	2006	F	PRT
p	PZ140	PAUL ARRAN	Netter	5.9	2.2	5	1978	F	GBR
p	PZ454	SUZIE	Liner	4.9	1.1	8	1974	F	GBR
p	Ex PZ1201	CACHALOT	De-registered	7.35	2.07	38	2002	G	GBR
p	Ex SS1	CORNISH CREST	De-registered	9.1	5.3	22	1946	W	GBR
p	SS1	BOY JAKE	Liner	4.83	1.12	6	1989	F	GBR
p	SS2	BLUE BELLE	Liner	5.5	1.7	19	2008	F	GBR
p	SS6	MOLLIE DAWN	Liner	4.54	0.55	7	2007	F	GBR
p	SS8	ASPER	Netter/Liner	9.2	7.2	164	1980	S	GBR
p	SS10	GIRL CHERRY	Liner	5.6	1.12	13.4	2012	F	GBR
p	SS17	OSPREY	Netter	5.0	0.8	60	1994	F	GBR
p	Ex SS21	HANNA G	De-registered	6.3	3.0	16	1992	F	GBR
p	SS25	KELLY GIRL	Liner	5.8	2.7	14	1981	F	GBR
p	SS35	MAGGIE	Liner	4.7	1	10	1991	F	GBR
p	SS41	SANDPIPER	Liner	5	1.1	7	1980	F	GBR
p	Ex SS42	SAFI	De-registered	5.9	1.3	30		F	PRT
p	SS46	MARY MO	Liner	5.46	1.24	41.25		F	GBR
p	Ex SS53	NORAH-T	De-registered	5.6	1.7	7	1987	F	GBR
p	Ex SS54	CALIOPE	De-registered	4.50	0.79	5	1980	F	
p	SS61	KEIRA	Liner	5.75	1.14	34.3	2011	F	GBR
p	Ex SS65	HOPE	De-registered	4.7	1.2	6	1991	F	GBR
p	Ex SS80	LITTLE CHRISTINA	De-registered	7.5	3.4	52	1972	W	GBR
p	SS80	LITTLE CHRISTINA (Ex SS104)	Netter/Liner	7.8	2.3	52	1989	F	GBR
p	Ex SS96	LADY ANNE	De-registered	5.2	1.3	8	1976		GBR
p	Ex SS112	JOHNATHAN SEAGULL	De-registered	5.2	1.2	52	1985	F	GBR
p	SS161	DIGNITY	Netter/Liner	8	6.2	45	2005	F	GBR
p	SS170	JEN	Liner	4.9	1.3	4	1985	F	GBR
p	SS209	STILL WATERS	Potter/liner	6.3	2.2	11	1975	F	
p	Ex SS221	JULIA NADINE	De-registered	4.3	0.8	12	1988	F	FRA
p	SS224	MARINER	Netter	5.1	0.8	22	1975	F	GBR
p	SS225	AGAN PROVIYAS (Ex PROVIDER)	Potter	5.6	1.8	6	1977	F	GBR
p	Ex SS227	AGAN DEVEDHEK	De-registered	4.8	1.1	6	1977	F	GBR
p	SS261	AMMO	Netter	4.9	0.7	59	1980	F	GBR
p	SS266	BELLE BETTINA	Netter	5.6	2.2	7	1978	F	GBR
p	SS665	BRISSONS	Liner	4.8	1.5	13	1990	F	GBR

ST IVES

p	SS681	LADY JOAN	Liner	5.7	1.8	9	1995	F	GBR
p	SS698	MIDNIGHT EXPRESS	To Ilfracombe	9.4	7.0	200	2001	F	GBR
p	SS711	BONITO	Liner/Angler	7.2	1.8	140	2003	F	GBR
p	SS716	SHIKARI	Liner	5.7	1.7	7	1980	F	GBR

St Ives can get very crowded with both boats & People!

NCI Station St Ives

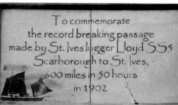

To commemorate
the record breaking passage
made by St. Ives lugger Lloyd SS5
Scarborough to St. Ives,
600 miles in 50 hours
in 1902

**An average speed of 12 knots
under sail!**

BR Poster for St Ives

FH506 Silver Lance - 19/09/2012

FY47 Our Liz - 03/09/2011

DH47 Autumn Silver II (Ex M & SS747) - 03/06/2009

M1103 Helen D - 03/07/2007

Ex PZ3 We're Here - 03/11/2011

PZ40 Gemma - 03/11/2011

PZ43 Daisy Mae - 03/06/2009

PZ49 Athena-Fay - 03/09/2011

PZ140 Paul Arran - 01/04/2008

PZ454 Suzie - 13/01/2012

PZ1201 Cachalot - 14/10/2008

Ex SS1 Cornish Crest - 19/09/2012

SS1 Boy Jack - 19/09/2012

SS2 Blue Belle - 05/04/2013

SS6 Mollie Dawn - 03/09/2011

SS8 Asper - 03/09/2011

SS10 Girl Cherry - 19/09/2012

SS17 Osprey - 03/09/2011

Ex SS21 Hanna G - 12/04/2010

SS25 Kelly Girl - 19/09/2012

SS35 Maggie - 03/09/2011

SS41 Sandpiper - 19/09/2012

Ex SS42 Safi - 03/07/2007

SS46 Mary Mo - 19/09/2012

SS53 Norah-T - 03/09/2011

Ex SS54 Caliope - 11/07/2008

SS61 Keira - 19/09/2012

Ex SS65 Hope - 03/06/2009

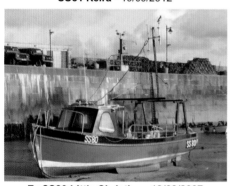

Ex SS80 Little Christina - 13/03/2007

SS80 (Ex SS104**) Little Christina** - 02/03/2009

Ex SS96 Lady Anne - 11/07/2008

Ex SS112 Johnathan Seagull - 03/06/2009

143

SS161 Dignity - 03/09/2011

SS170 Jen - 03/01/2011

SS209 Still Waters - 19/09/2012

SS224 Mariner - 19/09/2012

SS225 Agan Proviyas - 03/09/2011

Ex SS227 Agan Devedhek - 03/09/2011

SS261 Ammo - 03/06/2009

SS266 Belle Bettina - 19/09/2012

SS665 Brissons - 03/06/2009

SS681 Lady Joan - 03/01/2011

Ex SS698 Midnight Express - 29/09/2009

SS711 Bonito - 13/03/2007

SS713 Lyoness - 13/03/2007

SS716 Shikari - 03/01/2011

St Ives line up

145

Considerable Quay Space in Hayle

Fish Quay on left at Hayle – Looking South

In contrast to St Ives, Hayle was mainly a 19th century industrial port supporting the nearby mining industry. Two competing iron foundries were established at the port, and tin and copper smelting were carried out. Steel ships were built, and the steel for the Clifton Suspension Bridge at Bristol also came from Hayle. The shoaling entrance to the River Hayle from St Ives Bay was always a problem however, and the large dammed lake upstream from the quays was designed to flush out part of the shipping channel with the fast running ebb tide. Trade gradually declined through the 20th century, and the port finally ceased commercial operations in 1970. Few signs remain of its industrial past other than railway lines on the considerable quay space, of which the fishing industry has now taken advantage. There was an old partly filled in dry dock and the rotting gates have been recovered and put on display in the town. Some thirty fishing vessels operate from the port, netting, potting and line fishing, like St Ives. The port is dominated by the main line viaduct at the southern end. Major redevelopment to build a marina complex will soon have a dramatic effect on the appearance of the port. Just before work started on the Eastern quay in

Old dock gate

2012 a new fish landing area *(see left)* had been built but that is now no longer available. Plans also involve the central quay and work will soon start there as well. A crab and lobster processing plant is hidden in the sheds towards the end of the south eastern quay, and beyond that is a small boatyard which has a continual stream of fishing boats in for repair and also some fishing boat construction from scratch. In the western most outer harbour are a couple of floating holding cages for crab and lobster most of which are destined for the plant ashore.

Off loading onto East quay

Fish cages with processing plant in long shed behind and boatyard sheds to its left

River Hayle on left and Harbour Entrance on right

HAYLE FISHING VESSELS

P	PLN	VESSEL NAME	Type	LOA Mtrs	Reg Tons	Eng Kw	Year Built	Hull	Nat Build
p	CK930	SEA GLORY	Liner	6.82	0.7	130	1998	F	GBR
p	Ex FH273	SARAH JANE OF HELFORD	De-registered	7.5	7.9	140	1986	F	GBR
p	FY787	GRANDAD	Liner	5.48	1.9	11	1987	F	GBR
p	H145	SWIFT	Potter	9.99	8.2	187	1990	F	GBR
p	Ex LO59	GIRL LINDA	Decommissioned 2009	9.85	11.1	112	1992	F	GBR
p	PW469	FOR A FEW DOLLARS MORE	Liner	6	1.3	29	1991	F	GBR
p	PZ317	SEA SPIRIT	Dive Boat	6.5	0.7	45	2005	F	GBR
p	PZ318	SPRING TIDE	Liner	5.67	1.7	17	1971	W	
p	PZ379	BOY HARVEY	Potter/Liner	7.7	4.1	30	1973	F	GBR
p	PZ428	STERGAN	Liner	8.0	4.8	35	1974	F	GBR
p	PZ557	CELTIC BREEZE	Potter/Liner	7.3	4.2	42	1976	F	GBR
p	Ex PZ590	SHE WOLF	De-registered	9.9	6.6	158	1975	F	GBR
p	PZ695	JADE	Liner	5.9	1.4	5	1978	F	GBR
p	PZ1052	SEA MAIDEN	Netter/Liner	7.99	3.6	140	2011	F	GBR
p	PZ1187	GIRL STELLA	Netter	6.38	1.95	12	1949	W	GBR
p	PZ1191	SALLY ROSE OF NAVAX	Potter	7.3	1.5	40	0	F	GBR
p	SE10	BLUE PLOVER	Potter	6.5	4.0	25	1983	F	GBR
p	Ex SS12	WAVE DANCER	De-registered	4.85	0.6	34	1997	F	GBR
p	SS16	MY ROSS MIST	Potter/Liner	9.9	6.6	158	1975	F	GBR
p	SS24	JODA	Liner	6	1.3	60	2009	F	PRT
p	SS32	SEA BREEZE	Net/Potter/Liner	9	1.7	130	2006	F	GBR
p	SS66	PHRA - NANG	Potter	8.3	5.3	187	1990	F	GBR
p	SS88	TEGEN MOR	Netter/Potter/Liner	10.8	11.1	75	1985	G	GBR
p	SS262	ANNA MARIA	Potter/Liner	6.5	2.4	13	0	F	GBR
p	SS324	BRODI SEA	Netter/Liner	9.2	4	74	1979	F	GBR
p	SS673	MAID MEL (Ex M673)	Netter/Liner	5.7	1.7	13	1983	F	GBR
p	Ex SS685	FOU De BASSIN	De-registered	5.46	1.19	12		F	
p	SS697	ELLE V	Liner	6.9	1.0	55	2001	G	GBR
p	Ex SS704	CHLOE ESTELLE	De-registered	8.0	5.0	150	2002	F	GBR
p	SS707	ORCA	Netter/Liner	6.90	1.33	35	2002	G	GBR
p	SS710	SALLY	Potter	6.11	2.45	18	2002	G	GBR
p	Ex SS713	LYONESS	Liner	5.06	1.47	12	1993	F	GBR
p	SS713	LYONESS	Liner	5.95	1.21	29.8	2011	F	PRT
p	SS738	PROPER JOB	Liner	6.9	1.2	60	2004	F	GBR
p	SS744	SEA MAIDEN	Liner	6.8	1.1	74	2007	F	GBR
	SS762	KELLY MARIE	Potter	6.1	1.12	2.24	2005	F	GBR

CK930 Sea Glory - 05/04/2013

FH273 Sarah Jane of Helford - 29/08/2009

FY787 Grandad - 19/09/2012

H145 Swift - 29/08/2009

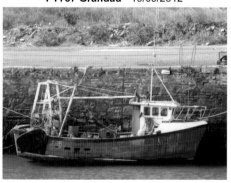

Ex LO59 Girl Linda - 01/04/2008

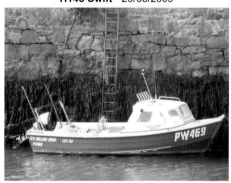

PW469 For a Few Dollars More - 19/09/2012

PZ317 Sea Spirit - 22/09/2012

PZ318 Spring Tide - 03/06/2009

PZ379 Boy Harvey - 03/01/2011

PZ428 Stergan - 03/01/2011

PZ557 Celtic Breeze - 01/04/2008

Ex PZ590 She Wolf - 01/04/2008

PZ695 Jade - 20/01/2013

PZ1052(Ex PD1052) **Sea Maiden** - 05/04/2013

PZ1187 Girl Stella - 28/10/2005

PZ1191 Sally Rose of Navax - 03/01/2011

SE10 Blue Plover - 03/01/2011

Ex SS12 Wave Dancer - 01/04/2008

SS16 My Ross Mist - 29/08/2009

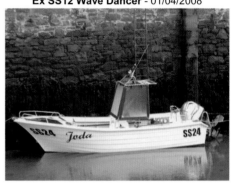

SS24 Joda - 03/01/2011

SS32 Sea Breeze - 29/08/2009

SS66 Phra-Nang - 26/11/2005

SS88 Tegen Mor - 01/04/2008

SS262 Anna Maria - 19/09/2012

SS324 Brodi Sea -12/04/2010

SS673 (Ex M673) **Maid Mel** - 03/01/2011

SS685 Fou de Bassin - 03/09/2011

SS697 Elle V - 29/08/2009

Ex SS704 Chloe Estelle - 01/04/2008

SS707 Orca - 19/09/2012

Ex SS713 Lyoness - 11/07/2008

SS713 Lyoness - 19/09/2012

SS738 Proper Job - 17/02/2009   **SS744 Sea Maiden** - 03/09/2011

**Fishing boats moored on central peninsular quay in the Inner harbour
with St Ives in centre distance and Eastern Quay
*(being developed on centre right)***

Outer harbour with fish/crab holding cages on the left

Entrance to Portreath – *White Signal Station centre right (arrowed)*

Looking into the Inner Harbour

Although a small fishing village from the early 17th century, Portreath became one of Cornwall's earliest industrial ports at the peak of the Cornish copper mining era in the 18th century. The original harbour was constructed in 1713 but only lasted until 1749, when it was rebuilt. The present pier was built in about 1760 to provide sheltered loading and unloading of vessels. It was extended in 1824. By 1800 there was a thriving seine fishing fleet operating, and the outer basin was completed at about the same time. The opening of the first Cornish railway- the Portreath Tramroad - between 1809-1812 and the linking of Portreath to the Hayle railway in 1837, made the construction of a second basin necessary. Cargoes of up to 100,000 tons of copper ore were exported to South Wales per year with coal imported on the return. Cheap coal in South Wales made it more economic to export the ore for smelting in Wales and only import the necessary coal to fuel the steam engines in the nearby copper mines. A housing estate now occupies the old storage yards. Both fishing and commercial operations declined with the slump in copper production in the late 1860's. WW1 and the depression in the 1920s meant that trade through the port had almost ceased by 1930. The harbour was taken over for exclusive use by the military during WW2 in association with the nearby airfield, stopping all commercial activities. After the war it was used by a few colliers until 1950. For several years only two fishing vessels operated from the port - lining, netting and potting, but in 2012 two more joined the fleet. The harbour is only accessible two hours either side of High Water, and is somewhat exposed to westerly winds and seas, when entry can be difficult.   Once inside the entrance breakwaters, which hug the eastern cliffs, a good sheltered inner harbour awaits. In the days of sail a system of flag signalling from the prominent lookout station *(White building arrowed in picture above)* on the north side of the harbour, assisted incoming vessels to make a safe entrance.   The white tower on top of the cliffs is a Day Mark *(Unlit)* to show the position of the port from seaward.

Harbour Entrance　　　　**Inner Harbour** (Centre right)

PORTREATH FISHING VESSELS

Photo	PLN	VESSEL NAME	Type	LOA Mtrs	Reg Tons	Eng Kw	Year Built	Hull	Nat Build
p	LL307	EARLY DAWN	Potter/Liner	8.2	4.88	59	1981	W	GBR
p	Ex PW287	LADY DI	De-registered	6.6	1.8	22	1981	F	GBR
p	Ex PZ86	SPILGARN	De-registered	4.5	0.8	6		F	
p	PZ93	ATLANTIC LASS	Potter	5.6	1.66	29.8	2008	F	GBR
p	TO3	LILY'S PRIDE	To Ilfracombe	6.6	1.9	32	2006	F	GBR
p	TO7	COSMO'S MARINER	Netter/Liner	6.95	2.2	27	2008	F	GBR
p	TO48	GOOD FORTUNE	Potter	7.99	2.68	104	2003	F	GBR

LL307 Early Dawn - 19/09/2012

Ex PW287 Lady Di - 03/07/2008

Ex PZ86 Spilgarn - 03/07/2008

PZ93 Atlantic Lass - 22/09/2012

TO3 Lily's Pride - 03/06/2009

TO7 Cosmo's Mariner - 19/09/2012

TO48 Good Fortune - 19/09/2012

A tricky approach on a prevailing wind lee shore

Porthreath
Inner Harbour

Remains of The harbour

Close up of the few blocks still standing

The two main working boats lined up on the beach

St Agnes grew up as a fishing and farming community but it was also a centre of the tin mining industry from Roman times to the 20th century. There have been five attempts to build a harbour at Trevaunance Cove which is just a short distance down the valley from St Agnes itself. The intention was for it to be an outlet on the north coast for Truro. Some attempts were more successful than others, and only a large number of stone blocks on the western side of the bay remain as testimony to the severe winter storms experienced on this coast. The first harbour was destroyed before completion in 1632 and the second lasted only a few months in 1684. A third was built using the expertise of the designer of the Eddystone lighthouse in 1699. This allowed fishing to prosper but it only lasted until 1705. The Tonkin family dominated the area and in 1709 they built a fourth harbour. The £6,000 cost bankrupted the Tonkin family and without maintenance the harbour was washed away in 1736. A more successful fifth attempt was made in 1798 by a newly formed St Agnes Harbour Company. This harbour with an outer northern pier protecting a smaller southern quay enabled the development of the Pilchard fishing industry, and the 17th Century 'Driftwood Spars' Hotel used to be a Pilchard cellar. Like Portreath, copper ore was exported to Wales and coal imported for the mines. Once again lack of maintenance was the harbour's undoing, and it was washed away in winter storms of 1915-16. A few small potters still operate from Trevaunace Cove during the summer months.

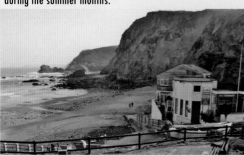

The attractive bay and Coastline

Driftwood Spars Hotel - The old fish cellar

ST AGNES FISHING VESSELS

Photo	PLN	VESSEL NAME	Type	LOA Mtrs	Reg Tons	Eng Kw	Year Built	Hull	Nat Build
p	SS120	BOTE	Potter	4.27	0.5	5	1963	F	GBR
p	SS247	WINKLE	Potter/liner	4.42	0.6	4	1978	W	GBR
p	TO10	SARAH JANE	Potter	4.93	0.6	6	1989	F	GBR
p	WY830	CHUTNEY	Liner	5.1	O.7	8	1999	F	GBR

SS120 Bote - 14/04/2008

SS247 Winkle - 03/06/2009

TO10 Sarah Jane - 03/07/2008

WY830 Chutney - 03/07/2008

Ready for work

157

The Harbour looking South

Looking East towards Porth

Newquay Harbour looking North East

Newquay was originally a small harbour in the 14th century providing a place of refuge on the wild north coast. It was developed to satisfy the mining and china clay industries, and avoid the treacherous passage round Lands End. Despite that, the 'New Quay' from which the town took its name was actually built in 1439!! The south pier was started in 1830, but only completed along with the north pier when under new ownership in 1840. A narrow gauge railway was constructed in 1849 which climbed to town level - near the present Morrisons store - through a steep 1 in 4.5 tunnel in the cliffs. When the island jetty was built in 1870 the railway crossed over to it on a wooden trestle bridge from the South Quay. There is an unusual 14th century 'Huer's Hut' on the cliffs just south of the town, which has a distinctly Mediterranean look about it. Seine fishing went on for many centuries, and there was an old fish cellar at the neck of the narrow peninsular west of the town near the old lifeboat house which boasted the steepest launching ramp in the country. Now a fleet of some 20 fishing vessels, mainly netting and potting with a little trawling and lining, operates from the harbour which dries out completely at low water. Registrations are very varied but the 'PW' from nearby Padstow predominates.

Colourful Line ups

NEWQUAY FISHING VESSELS

Photo	PLN	VESSEL NAME	Type	LOA Mtrs	Reg Tons	Eng Kw	Year Built	Hull	Nat Build
p	AB199	PATHFINDER	To Bangor, N Wales	8.5	6.3	82	1987	F	GBR
p	Ex BM502	SALAMANDER	De-registered	9.5	9.9	95	1974	F	GBR
p	BS422	BOY DARREN	Potter	6.4	1.4	37	1991	F	GBR
p	E6	EVELYN	Potter	7.9	1	67	2001	F	GBR
p	FH222	SUNDOWNER	Netter/Potter	9.30	3.29	53	1977	F	GBR
p	Ex FH289	ELIZABETH MADELINE	De-registered	8.5	2.3	53	1974	F	GBR
p	GY18	PROVIDER	Potter	5.84	1.1	7	1987	F	GBR
p	HL1059	CYCLONE	Netter	8.1	3.8	175	1995	F	GBR
p	Ex IH180	BAND OF HOPE	De-registered	9.9	9.9	97	1977	F	GBR
p	NN18	QUANTUS	Netter/Potter	7.07	1.6	26	1997	F	GBR
p	Ex PH381	DIONNE	To Portree	7.8	4.7	86	1980	F	GBR
p	Ex PH583	SURFHUNTER	De-registered	7.15	1.7	22	1986	F	GBR
p	PW16	TIZZARDLEE-ON	Netter/Potter	9.3	5.3	88	2008	F	GBR
p	PW17	GAL CADORA (Ex OB158)	Potter	10.4	9.3	96	1990	F	GBR
p	PW22	GOOD INTENT	Potter	7.96	3.5	140	2009	F	GBR
p	Ex PW107	TALLULA	De-registered	9.3	6.6	90	1990	W	GBR
p	PW122	ZARVAN	Netter/Potter	8.1	6.5	205	1988	F	GBR
p	PW289	BOSCASTLE PEGANINA	Potter	9.31	6.6	90	1990	F	GBR
p	Ex PW412	HELEN JANE	Decommissioned 2009	9.65	9.06	140	1990	F	GBR
p	Ex PW432	CHE SARA SARA	De-registered	9.8	3.9	200	1977	F	GBR
p	PZ30	LOYAL PARTNER	Netter/Potter	10.7	10.4	97	1963	S	NLD
p	PZ480	KELYN MOR	To Brixham	4.6	0.9	5	1974	F	GBR
p	PZ682	HELONA	To Plymouth	5.75	2	22	1980	F	GBR
p	SS13	SWEET AS	To North Shields	5.95	2	26		F	
p	SS40	TOLLBAR	Liner	5.80			2005	F	GBR
p	Ex SS40	SHAMROCK	De-registered	5.6	1.8	13	1980	F	GBR
p	SS45	SHANNON	Netter/Potter	9.2	2.8	164	1998	F	GBR
p	SS233	TRYPHENA	Liner	5.6	1.7	5	1978	F	GBR
p	TH288	GOLDEN LANCER	Netter/Potter	9.9	9.3	81	1982	F	GBR
p	Ex YH1	PIONEER	De-registered	9.2	5.7	55		F	GBR

Huer's Hut

Sign on Huer's Hut

BM502 Salamander - 13/09/2008

BS422 Boy Darren - 15/06/2012

E6 Evelyn - 27/09/2012

FH222 Sundowner - 28/10/2009

Ex FH289 Elizabeth Madeline - 10/10/2007

GY18 Provider - 09/09/2011

HL1059 Cyclone - 27/09/2012

Ex IH180 Band of Hope - 13/09/2008

NN18 Quantus - 09/09/2011

Ex PH381 Dionne - 29/05/2007

Ex PH583 Surfhunter - 27/04/2007

PW16 Tizzardly-On! - 28/10/2009

PW17 (Ex OB158) **Gal Cadora** - 27/09/2012

PW22 Good Intent - 28/10/2009

Ex PW91 Spirit of Cornwall - 27/04/2007

Ex PW107 Tallula - 27/09/2012

PW122 Zarvan - 28/10/2009

PW289 Boscastle Peganina - 28/04/2006

Ex PW412 Helen Jane - 26/10/2007

Ex PW432 Che Sara Sara - 27/04/2007

PZ30 Loyal Partner - 15/02/2008

PZ480 Kelyn Mor - 27/09/2012

SS13 Sweet As - 09/09/2011

SS40 Tollbar - 27/09/2012

SS45 Shannon - 30/05/2007

SS84 Three Jays - 23/01/2010

SS233 Tryphena - 09/09/2011

TH288 Golden Lancer - 23/01/2010

Ex YH1 Pioneer - 28/10/2009

Looking Upstream (*Padstow on Right*)   **A distant 'Doom Bar'** (*from War Memorial*)

As one of the few sheltered havens on the North coast, Padstow, located two miles up the River Camel, has a long history as a commercial port, the first pier being built in 1536. It is the largest port in North Cornwall, but the sand bars that developed to produce 'Doom Bar' at the river entrance in the mid 19th century restricted its continued development as a major port. In 1829, capstans were positioned on Stepper Point at the mouth of the river to assist ships warping into and out of the river estuary. Over the centuries it has been used for the export of slate, tin, and copper, and when the London & South Western Railway arrived in 1899 it provided an outlet for china clay and a ready access to London's Billingsgate fish market for the herring industry. The line was a victim of the Beeching closures in 1966. Now, as well as being used for fishing, the harbour mostly exports sand from the estuary for agriculture. Local fishing is mainly for lobsters and crabs within the River Camel. Only seven boats of the fleet are now of 10 metres length or more *(down from 10 in 2006)*, and these larger craft operate much further afield. The long outer harbour called 'South Dock' almost dries out at low water so many of the larger vessels dock in the inner floating harbour where a submersible lock gate maintains a higher level as the tide ebbs. About 33 vessels operate from the port, most of which bear the 'PW' registration but there are many visitors from various SW ports and sometimes from further afield. There are fewer trawlers now and most boats are engaged in potting and netting. The larger vessels may sometimes be seen at Newlyn. Some boats may be found amongst the many pleasure craft at Rock, a resort on the opposite side of the River Camel. In 2000 the National Lobster Hatchery was opened at the southern end of the harbour where lobsters are bred. When large enough they are taken out to suitable breeding grounds where they are released either by divers or pumped down to the seabed from the surface by fishing vessels and they will take about 5 years to reach commercial size for landing.

South Dock - Ferry Jetty to 'Rock' on left

South dock *from south*

PADSTOW FISHING VESSELS

P	PLN	VESSEL NAME	Type	LOA Mtrs	Reg Tons	Eng Kw	Year Built	Hull	Nat Build
p	BA284	VIKING	To Belfast	9.84	9.9	93	1987	S	GBR
p	Ex DR166	GIPSY KING	De-registered	7.4	3.8	50	1992	F	GBR
p	E524	SHAMROCK	Potter	8	1.6	88	2008	F	GBR
p	FH229	NEWLEK-MOR	Potter	4.97	1.09	9	2000	W	GBR
p	FY529	VESTA	Potter	7.10	3.2	19	1979	W	GBR
p	FY776	TREWARTHA	Potter	6.0	2.8	22	1993	F	GBR
p	Ex IH318	AMBER MIST	To Ireland	9.9	11	95		S	
p	M99	VERONICA ANN	Potter	11.6	24.66	129	1992	F	GBR
p	Ex PH24	SU JEAN	Decommissioned	9.75	7.4	95	1979	F	GBR
p	PW1	BERLEWEN	Netter	14.97	49.0	204	2003	S	GBR
p	PW6	SHANMAR	Liner	5.02	0.93	4.47	1995	F	
p	Ex PW10	EMMA KATE	De-registered	8.80	5.6	59	1982	W	GBR
p	PW11	CORNISH ROSE	Liner	4.72	1.14	11.8	2000	F	GBR
p	PW14	MAID OF BODINNICK (Ex FY195)	Crabber	6.6	2.3	6	1972	W	GBR
p	Ex PW15	TIME BANDIT	De-registered	5.92	1.5	13	2002	F	
p	Ex PW15	GIRL SHARON	De-registered	6.39	1.74	23	2002	F	GBR
p	PW21	CELTIC BREEZE (Ex AB214)	Potter	6.24	1.3	32	2003	F	GBR
p	Ex PW24	OUR KATY	De-registered	5.60	1.5	10	1978	F	GBR
p	PW27	PROVIDER	Trawler	11.1	15.1	86.5	1990	F	GBR
p	PW28	OUR ZOE	Potter	7.4	23.76	50	1992	F	GBR
p	PW30	MISTY BLUE	Liner	6	1.46	56	2008	F	GBR
p	Ex PW36	LE LOUSTIC	De-registered	5.9	1.4	44.7	1999	F	GBR
p	PW37	AMY O	Angler	4.85	0.73	8.75	2002	F	FIN
p	PW45	CHARISMA (Ex BA45)	Netter/Tuna Liner	16.43	37.9	268	1999	S	GBR
p	PW46	ROAMS (Ex PT46 & PW463)	Potter	4.84	1.24	29.5	1998	F	GBR
p	PW50	CHANTELLE (Ex LK50)	Potter	10.60	15.3	129	1989	F	GBR
p	PW72	BOY REGGIE	Liner	4.2	0.6	10.9	2010	F	GBR
p	PW77	GIRL RACHEL	Netter/Liner	9.95	4.1	112	1987	F	GBR
p	PW95	ELEANOR ROGET	Potter	10.12	5.1	94	1989	S	GBR
p	PW124	HELEN JANE II	Netter	9.8	9.1	107	2003	F	GBR
p	Ex PW132	HOMARUS	De-registered	7.8	4.25	80	1979	F	GBR
p	PW214	THOMAS ANDREW	Netter	9.83	4.5	81	2004	F	GBR
p	PW333	DAYMER BAY	Netter/Potter	8.00	6.3	60	1982	F	GBR
p	PW392	ERINDORS	Netter	5.13	0.9	14	1993	F	GBR
p	PW458	ORIENT	Trawler/Scalloper	8.4	5.75	96	1988	F	GBR
p	PW460	BLUE FOX	Angler	8.20	2.0	135	1991	F	GBR
p	PW474	JACQUELINE	Angler	6.78	2.7	22	1965	W	GBR
p	PW485	SPINDRIFT	Angler	5.64	1.2	37	1991	F	GBR
p	PZ83	LOUELLA	Liner	4.45	0.7	7.4	1978	F	GBR
p	PZ125	PATRICE	Netter/Potter	8.00	4.05	41	1988	F	GBR
p	TH177	ICTHUS	Potter	12.20	26.0	187	1990	F	GBR
p	TN104	BON AMY (Ex PW470)	To Fraserburgh	8.25	4.9	63	2006	F	GBR
p	TO46	SHAMROCK	Netter	5.95	1.77	27		F	
p	WH111	BETHANY J	Potter	8.4	2.7	138	1994	F	GBR

BA284 Viking - 14/10/2010

Ex DR166 Gipsy King - 21/07/2011

E524 Shamrock - 21/07/2011

FY529 Vesta - 23/03/2013

FY776 Trewartha - 23/03/2013

Ex IH318 Amber Mist - 23/01/2010

M99 Veronica Ann - 23/03/2013

Ex PH24 Su Jean - 06/09/2005

PW1 Berlewen - 03/09/2011

PW6 Shanmar - 20/03/2013

Ex PW10 Emma Kate II - 20/02/2009

PW11 Cornish Rose - 20/03/2013

PW14 (Ex FY195) **Maid of Bodinnick** - 21/07/2011

Ex PW15 Time Bandit - 13/09/2008

Ex PW15 Girl Sharron - 20/03/2013

PW21 (Ex AB214) **Celtic Breeze** - 28/10/2009

PW22 Good Intent - 28/10/2009

Ex PW24 Our Katy - 21/07/2011

PW27 Provider - 23/03/2013

PW28 Our Zoe - 23/03/2013

PW30 Misty Blue - 21/07/2011

Ex PW36 Le Loustic - 26/10/2007

PW37 Amy O - 27/05/2005

PW45 (Ex BA45) **Charisma** - 15/06/2012

PW46 (Ex PT46) **Roams** - 27/09/2012

PW50 (Ex LK50) **Chantelle** - 27/09/2012

PW72 Boy Reggie - 27/09/2012

PW77 Girl Rachel - 23/03/2013

PW95 Elinor Roget - 13/09/2008

PW124 Helen Jane II - 15/06/2012

Ex PW132 Homarus - 15/06/2012

PW214 Thomas Andrew - 26/10/2007

PW333 Daymer Bay - 26/10/2010

PW392 Erindors - 28/10/2009

PW458 Orient - 15/07/2008

PZ460 Blue Fox - 23/01/2010

PW474 Jacqueline - 23/01/2010

PW485 Spindrift - 20/03/2013

PZ83 Louella - 20/03/2013

PZ125 Patrice - 23/01/2010

TH177 Icthus - 23/03/2013

TN104 (Ex PW104) **Bon Amy** - 23/01/2010

TO46 Shamrock - 23/03/2013

WH111 Bethany-J - 13/09/2008

Floating Dock - From Inside

A Brixham based Beam Trawler leaving

The Gate Submerging

View of Bay from Port Quin

Port Quin - Landward View

View from buildings

Port Quin *(originally called Porthqueen)* is another attractive almost disused fishing hamlet set in a deep bay between Padstow and Port Isaac. It is said that fishing stopped after all the local men were lost in a major storm in 1698, leaving only the women and children but this may have happened 100 years later. The old fish cellars can be seen here, though many have undergone conversion to holiday homes. Most of the buildings and land are owned by the National Trust. At the head of the harbour is a stone post near the high water mark which was some kind of boundary marker. One small potter is kept ashore under cover, and launched as required.

Marker Post in foreground

Converted buildings

PORT QUIN FISHING VESSEL

Photo	PLN	VESSEL NAME	Type	LOA Mtrs	Reg Tons	Eng Kw	Year Built	Hull	Nat Build
p	PW56	DARING	Potter	5.15	0.9	44	1984	F	GBR

PW56 Daring - 08/09/2008

Port Isaac - looking West

Port Isaac - Entering harbour

Port Isaac *(originally known as Porthissek)* is a traditional fishing village set in a fairly deep bay facing north on the North Cornish coast with many of the old fishing industry buildings still in situ. Delabole slate also used to be exported from here to both France and Belgium. The harbour dries out at low water as seen above. A short pier was built in the 16th century, and in the mid 19th century the village supported as many as 50 fishing vessels, and four fish cellars. In 1815 one cellar alone recorded packing 1400 hogsheads of pilchards in one week which is approximately four million fish!! The old 18th century curing cellars in the South West corner of the harbour are the only fish cellars in Cornwall which are still in use. Tubs of salted mackerel can still be seen there, though the mackerel are waiting to be used solely for baiting the lobster pots. The inshore lifeboat now occupies another of the old fish cellars. To the north of the pedestrian causeway in the harbour are what look like rock pools, but these were actually the old 'Keep Pools' to keep catches fresh until ready for marketing. The present breakwaters were only built in the 1930s. About nine potters operate from the harbour for crab and lobster, many of which are sold direct from the old cellars. Any other fish bought here however, have been imported from Newlyn or Plymouth!! Most of the boats carry the 'PW' Padstow registration, often thought of as '**P**ort **W**enn' since the village has been used as the setting for ITV's 'Doc Martin'. It is also the base for the very successful Fishermens' Choir

'Doc Martin's House'

Fish Cellar

The Beach slipway at High Tide

Fishing Boats moored Off the beach

The Fish Cellar

PORT ISAAC FISHING VESSELS

Photo	Reg	VESSEL NAME	Type	LOA Mtrs	Reg Tons	Eng KW	Year Built	Hull	Nat Build
p	PW5	HELEN CLAIRE	Potter	9.66	8	228	2006	F	GBR
p	PW20	JANICE MARY	Potter	6.00	0.80	15	2002	F	
p	PW100	OUR BELLE ANN	Potter	11.73	7.5	373	1980	F	GBR
p	PW104	SHARICMAR	Potter	8.22	5.9	190	1988	F	GBR
p	PW163	FREE SPIRIT	Potter	9.95	6.95	218	2007	F	GBR
p	PW235	BOY JOHN II	Potter	5.33	1.5	44	1980	F	GBR
	PW242	OUR WINNIE	Potter	3.96	0.36	1	1965	W	GBR
p	PW364	ORCADES II	Potter	12.19	4.4	228	2001	S	NLD
p	Ex PW429	HELEN CLARE II	De-registered	10.00	4.8	179	1994	F	GBR
p	Ex PW433	TIGGER	De-registered	6.9	1.5	44	2007	F	GBR
p	PW446	FREE SPIRIT	Potter	8.50	3.4	231	1988	G	GBR
p	YH299	MARY D	Potter	8.51	4.7	89	1989	F	

PW5 Helen Clare - 27/07/2007

PW20 Janice Mary - 27/05/2005

PW100 Our Belle Anne - 14/10/2011

PW104 Sharicmar - 20/03/2013

PW163 Free Spirit - 27/07/2007

PW235 Boy John II - 14/10/2011

PW364 Orcades II - 27/07/2007

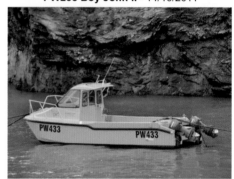

Ex PW433 Tigger - 27/07/2007

YH299 Mary D - 14/10/2011

Harbour entrance

Port Gaverne   **Port Gaverne Fish Cellars**

Port Gaverne *(originally Port Kerne)* is a hamlet at the end of a bay just to the east of Port Isaac. Until the pier was built at Port Isaac it was the more important harbour with four large fish cellars which processed up to 1,000 tons of pilchards in the early 19th century when they sold at about £40 per ton. The old fishermens' buildings and the fish cellars can still be seen. Surprisingly Port Gaverne could take larger vessels than Port Isaac and in the early 19th century before the advent of the railways it was the main port for the export of Delabole slate and the import of Welsh coal using vessels in excess of 100 tons displacement. Only one small potter operates from here in the summer but it may often be seen in Port Isaac.

PORT GAVERNE FISHING VESSELS

Photo	PLN	VESSEL NAME	Type	LOA Mtrs	Reg Tons	Eng Kw	Year Built	Hull	Nat Build
p	Ex PW455	LENNY P	De-registered	4.93	0.83	9	2003	G	GBR
p	YH563	HIGHLIGHT	Potter	4.91	0.9	11		F	GBR

Ex PW455 Lenny P - 08/09/2008   **YH563 Highlight** - 08/09/2008

The old quay carved out of the rocks

Lined up

BOSCASTLE

Boscastle Entrance looking North

The Breakwaters looking West

Boscastle was an impossible harbour to sail in or out of due to its twisting channel surrounded by high ground. Sailing vessels were therefore warped in and out using a so called 'Hobbling Boat' to lay an anchor ahead of the boat, after which a shore party marched backwards pulling the boat forward via a pulley attached to the anchor. Despite these problems this attractive cove was used until 1920 commercially for the export of metal ores and china clay from Bodmin Moor. It did however support its own rather unsuccessful 'Seine' in the early 19th century.   It was more successful when mackerel chased sprats into the harbour on a rising tide and nets across the harbour mouth caught the mackerel on the ebb!   Boscastle is however exposed to the Atlantic swells, and piers were built in the 16th century and restored in 1740 to protect the cove from the sea.   It was from the landward side that the port suffered most however, when flash flooding occurred in 2004, with dramatic helicopter rescues for many of the holidaymakers and inhabitants.   The two resident fishing craft were out at sea at the time and could not believe the radio messages that cars were being swept out to sea. This flooding effectively closed the port until the channel was dug out during 2005.   Once usable again the two resident vessels were able to move back from Padstow from which they had temporarily been operating. Boscastle has been restored to its pristine attractive condition, though there is some controversy over the rather more modern looking bridge over the stream entering the harbour.   There are now three small potters operating from the port.

Empty harbour scene in winter   **A busier harbour scene in summer**

BOSCASTLE FISHING VESSELS

P	Reg	VESSEL NAME	Type	LOA Mtrs	Reg Tons	Eng Kw	Year Built	Hull	Nat Build
p	E507	THREE JAYS	Potter	7.6	3.6	30		F	
p	E519	RENE	Potter	5.96	210	25	2005	F	GBR
p	FH30	AUTUMN ROSE (Ex KY30)	Potter	6.55	1.9	39	2002	F	GBR
p	Ex M3	INDUSTRIOUS	To 3 Rivers	9.98	5.8	231	2004	F	GBR
p	PW10	BLUE DIAMOND (Ex KY1001)	To Scarborough	6.44	1.8	23	2000	F	GBR
p	EX SE8	EDWARD J (Ex PZ1174)	To Oban	6.5	2.7	24		F	GBR

E507 Three Jays - 02/09/2012

E519 Rene - 21/03/2009

FH30 (Ex KY30) **Autumn Rose** - 02/09/2012

Ex M3 Industrious - 21/03/2009

PW10 (Ex KY1001) **Blue Diamond** - 27/05/2005

Ex SE8 (Ex PZ1174) **Edward J** - 28/04/2006

Dramatic Coastline

The River Quay Outside Bude Sea Lock
(Note Railway lines)

Bude Channel

The 20 ft tidal range at Bude is the largest in Cornwall. The effects of this were alleviated to some extent by the construction of the Bude Canal in 1823. This resulted in a harbour side within a sea lock, that was free from the tidal rise and fall. The entrance was protected from the Atlantic swell by a breakwater made of natural stone which connected the mainland to several rocks off the entrance. It was originally built in 1812 and rebuilt in 1838. Wooden posts down the west side of the channel were used as haulage posts in the days of sail, to winch boats in and out of the entrance channel. Although the canal itself ceased commercial operations in 1890, the upper and lower basins were a hive of commercial activity with even ship building taking place in the upper basin. Coal, limestone and cargoes from South Wales were imported, while grain and oak bark for tanning leather were exported to ports up the Bristol Channel. The present road bridge which replaced a swing bridge in about 1950 denies nautical access to the upper basin, but the quarter of a mile length between the sea lock and the low road bridge has since been maintained as a sheltered harbour, and commercial operation only ceased in 1940. There is talk of renewing the opening bridge once again. The river quay outside the canal *(but just up river from the lock)* was used with a narrow gauge railway, part of which can still be seen on the quay. Railway tipper trucks offloaded directly into barges on the river. There are still a few small fishing vessels operating from the port, mainly involved in potting for crab and lobster. They moor below the lock for most of the summer months, and retreat into the canal basin for the winter. The fish quay is beside the lock. The 'PW' (Padstow) registration is predominant, and those that re-registered with Welsh registrations have come back to the Padstow registrations.

Bude Breakwater from the Lock
(Left)

Bude Basin below the Bridge
(Right)

The Entrance Channel

The Breakwater protecting the Channel (on the right)

BUDE FISHING VESSELS

Photo	PLN	VESSEL NAMES	Type	LOA Mtrs	Reg Tons	Eng Kw	Year Built	Hull	Nat Build
p	Ex PT57	MAKO OF BUDE (Ex PW431)	De-registered	7.75	1.6	112	1992	F	GBR
p	Ex PW25	SAN MARIA	De-registered	6.22	1.9	26	1976	F	GBR
p	PW41	BLACK PEARL	Potter	4.9	0.96	13.4	1985	F	GBR
p	PW43	TWILIGHT (Ex CK3)	Potter/	5.7	0.9	37	2004	F	GBR
p	PW44	ELLEN MARY (Ex PT43 & PW437)	Potter	5.40	1.4	6	1968	F	GBR
p	PW456	LILY MAY II	Potter	6.9	1.8	65	2003	F	GBR
p	Ex WH454	T.K.	De-registered	6.2	1.7	116	1983	F	GBR
p	YH2489	HAPPY DAYS	Potter	4.9	0.6	5	1974	F	GBR

Ex PT57 (Ex PW431) **Mako of Bude** - 11/05/2009

Ex PW25 San Maria - 10/05/2010

PW41 Black Pearl - 02/03/2012

PW43 (Ex CK3) **Twilight** - 11/05/2009

THE PORT AND CANAL

In 1820 The Bude Harbour and Canal Company took over the Haven and built a "Pier" to protect the new Canal Sea Lock and altered the course of the river. In 1838 the Pier was swept away and the present Breakwater was built in its place.

Two large Basins were constructed for the ships to discharge their cargoes which were mainly coal, limestone and general or "Bristol Goods". The main exports were grain and oak bark used for tanning leather.

In the Upper Basin a Shipyard was established with a Steam Saw Mill for ships timbers. More than a dozen ships were built there in the 19th century, being launched sideways into the Canal.

Whilst the trade on the Canal diminished the number of ships using the Port increased which continued in general use up until the Second World War. The Canal Sea Lock is still in use today.

PW44 (Ex PT43 & PW437) **Ellen Mary** - 02/03/2012   **PW456 Lily May II** - 02/03/2012

Ex WH454 T.K. - 11/05/2009   **YH2489 Happy Days** - 19/02/2011

Fishing Boats outside the Sea Lock *(Note Channel markers on right)*

The original port for the islands was on St Mary's at Old Town. This was a small harbour built in the 13th century serving the nearby castle, of which only the Motte now remains. The old harbour wall can clearly be seen at low water. An old lead salting cask was found at the end of the quay providing evidence that salting of fish took place in Old Town. However fishing has always been on a subsistence basis on the islands and in spite of one unsuccessful attempt to establish a commercial operation in the 19th century it has virtually remained that way. However during the peak of the pilchard and herring seasons the islands' waters were often 'invaded' by commercial fishing fleets from the mainland. Some shellfish are now sent over to the market at Newlyn. The number of fishing vessels active on the islands has reduced to 18 from 29 in 2006. They consist of netters and potters in the main and no longer any trawlers. One is used for beach seining for mullet on St Martins. Most of them bear the 'SC' (Scilly) registration. The helicopter link to Tresco and St Marys has now terminated and while there are plans to improve the ferry terminal facilities at the end of St Mary's Quay there is much discussion about the Penzance harbour terminal jeopardising the main link to the mainland but some solution must be found.

St Mary's Quay across to Rat Island

St Mary's (Original Harbour wall in foreground)

St Mary's. The main harbour on St Mary's was originally built in 1601. Further works extended it northwards across to a small rock called Rat Island between 1836 and 1839 to form the quay as it now is, though further work was carried out in 1889 and the mid 1940s. The main reason for the improvements was nothing to do with fishing but to provide shelter for the ferry service and to cope with the increasing trade in flowers to the mainland. Most of the fishing vessels are between 8-10metres in length but there are a few smaller craft, which on Cornwall would be known as 'Toshers', but on the islands are called 'Punts'. Two 'Punts' no longer registered ,operate from bays on the East side of the island at Watermill Cove and Porth Hellick. At the latter is a memorial to where one Admiral of the Fleet Sir Cloudesley Shovell's body came ashore in 1707 after wrecking his flagship HMS 'Association', just one of the many shipwrecks round these coasts, most without memorials.

St Marys from North west

Old Quay – Watermill Cove

Porth Hellick

St Martins. Only six craft now operate from St Martins, though fish catches are offloaded in St Mary's. Four of them moor in the shelter of Higher Town Quay, while two 'Punts' operate from the beach at Lower Town. SC4 the 'Rockhopper' is sometimes used for beach seining for mullet.

St Martins Higher Town Quay

St Martins Lower Town Quay looking South to St Marys

Tresco and Bryher The original names for these two islands in the early 17th century were 'Treskay' and 'Brear'. Only one modern fishing vessel, used for netting and potting, now operates from the small harbour at New Grimsby. This is in the sheltered New Grimsby Sound between the islands of Tresco and Bryher. The Sound is quite shallow and the harbour dries out at low water. Two castles which protect the Tresco channel have interesting Royalist and Parliamentarian history, and date back to the 17th century. There is evidence of fish cellars having existed on Tresco as another word for a fish cellar is 'Pallass' which has been corrupted to 'Palace' and there is both a 'Palace Road' and 'Palace Inn' on Tresco. There is certainly no palace in the accepted sense on the island!!

Tresco - New Grimsby Harbour

New Grimsby Sound
(*Cromwell's Castle on Right*)

It is regretted that since the helicopter operation stopped in 2013 there is now no direct link to Tresco from the mainland.

St Agnes Two potters operate from St Agnes. One from the sheltered quay in Port Conger on the north side of the island into which the island ferries operate, and the other on the more exposed side at Periglis. Periglis has two disused lifeboat slipways and the older one was the longest in the UK. During WW2 a German bomber dropped his load in the harbour, injuring one fisherman. The German pilot apparently reported a successful mission against a major port!! As for the fisherman, in 2006, he was still mending the nets for his son who operates the well used vessel SC41 'Pioneer' even though over 80 years of age. He has since died, but the next generation father and son still operate the boat. Port Conger has an old Custom House which was used to try and prevent the thriving 19th century smuggling trade from France. It now has a more popular use as the well known 'Turks Head' public house. The chef operates SC181 appropriately called the 'Turks Head'.

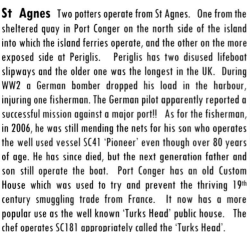

St Agnes - Periglis Harbour & Lifeboat Slipway

ISLES OF SCILLY FISHING VESSELS

P	HOME PORT	PLN	VESSEL NAME	Type	LOA Mtrs	Reg Tons	Eng Kw	Year Built	Hull	Nat Build
p	ST MARYS	BD279	CERI LEE	Potter	4.45	0.7	5	1989	F	GBR
p	Ex TRESCO	FY125	SOUTHERN STAR	To Plymouth	9.73	10.5	90	1990	F	GBR
p	ST MARYS	Ex M65	SUNSTAR	De-registered	8.53	0.58	7	1978	G	GBR
p	ST MARTINS	PW23	SARAFINE (Ex LAURA B)	Netter/Potter	7.15	3.59	47	1977	W	GBR
p	ST MARYS	PZ734	CYNTH	Potter	4.50	9.94	90	-	W	UNK
p	ST MARTINS	Ex SC2	LOWENA	De-registered	6.69	1.25	16	1997	F	GBR
p	ST MARTINS	SC4	ROCKHOPPER	Seiner/Potter	4.73	2.16	9	1954	W	GBR
p	TRESCO	Ex SC8	SAMSON	De-registered	7.68	0.93	13	1991	W	GBR
p	ST MARYS	SC11	VICTORY of HELFORD	Netter	10.73	8.79	103	1975	W	GBR
p	ST MARTINS	SC16	NORTHERN STAR	Liner/Potter	4.45	1.15	3	1990	F	GBR
p	ST MARYS	SC17	ATLANTIS	To Eyemouth	6.43	2.19	11	1971	W	GBR
p	ST MARYS	Ex SC22	PENGUIN	De-registered	7.92	1.55	8	1973	W	GBR
p	ST MARYS	SC32	VICKY ANNA	Netter/Potter	9.78	1.05	88	1985	F	GBR
p	BRYHER	SC35	EMERALD DAWN	Potter	7.77	2.74	8	1946	W	GBR
p	ST AGNES	SC41	PIONEER	Netter/Potter	8.02	2.78	7	1900	W	GBR
p	Ex ST MARYS	SC46	SWAN DANCER	To Campbelltown	9.75	0.86	58	1992	F	FRA
p	ST MARYS	SC70	CURLEW	Potter	8.23	4.13	9	1948	W	GBR
p	ST MARTINS	SC76	PELICAN	Potter	4.46	0.73	19	1993	F	GBR
p	ST MARYS	Ex SC163	KAMERUKA	De-registered	7.40	1.02	45	1990	F	GBR
p	BRYHER	SC167	MAIDEN BOWER	Potter	7.92	1.73	7	-	F	GBR
p	ST MARTINS	SC168	BOY ADAM	Potter	4.73	1.79	7	1973	F	GBR
p	Ex TRESCO	Ex SC169	LORRAINE RUTH	To Ayr	8.28	1.29	7	1985	F	GBR
p	ST MARYS	Ex SC172	PONTIOUS	De-registered	6.2	1.8	14	2004	F	GBR
p	ST MARTINS	SC173	RESOLUTION	Netter/Potter	7.95	3.1	37	2004	F	GBR
p	ST MARYS	Ex SC175	MARAUDER	To N Shields	9.96	9.1	84	2005	F	GBR
p	ST MARYS	SC177	GALLOS	Netter/Potter	7.36	3.1	53	2004	F	GBR
p	ST MARYS	SS149	MARANATHA	Potter	5.94	0.65	7	1965	W	GBR
	ST AGNES	SC180	TURKS HEAD	Potter	4.75	0.67	7		F	GBR
		SC187	MADELEINE	Potter	4.86	1.13	6	1995	F	GBR
p	Ex ST MARTINS	TH424	KAY-LARIE (Ex SU414)	To Newlyn ?	6.6	3.5	41	1978	F	GBR
p	ST MARYS	Ex WH606	LITTLE LAUREN	De-registered	4.8	1	8	1990	F	GBR

Note: TH424 has been sold & left the islands - possibly to Newlyn.

St Agnes - Port Conger

BD279 Ceri-Lee - 14/01/2009

FY125 Southern Star - 07/07/2008

Ex M65 Sunstar - 10/07/2008

PW23 Sarafine (*Ex Laura B*) - 05/10/2005

Ex PW461 Gwendra - 08/10/2005

PZ734 Cynth - 10/07/2008

Ex SC2 Lowena - 05/10/2005

SC4 Rockhopper - 05/10/2005

Ex SC8 Samson - 06/10/2005

SC11 Victory of Helford - 11/08/2008

SC16 Northern Star - 08/07/2008

SC17 Atlantis - 09/10/2005

Ex SC22 Penguin - 03/10/2005

SC32 Vicky Anna - 05/10/2005

SC35 Emerald Dawn - 05/10/2005

SC41 Pioneer - 07/10/2005

Ex SC46 Swan Dancer - 07/07/2008

SC70 Curlew - 07/07/2008

SC76 Pelican - 05/10/2005

Ex SC163 Kameruka - 03/10/2005

SC167 Maiden Bower - 09/07/2008

SC168 Boy Adam - 08/07/2008

Ex SC169 Lorraine Ruth - 07/07/2008

Ex SC172 Pontious - 06/07/2008

SC173 Resolution - 05/10/2005

SC175 Marauder - 05/07/2008

SC177 Gallos - 10/07/2008

SS149 Maranatha - 03/09/2011

TH424 Kay-Larie - 05/04/2013

Ex WH606 Little Lauren - 20/07/2011

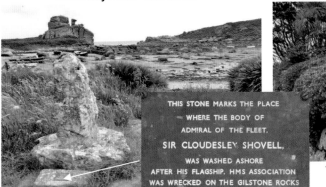

THIS STONE MARKS THE PLACE WHERE THE BODY OF ADMIRAL OF THE FLEET, SIR CLOUDESLEY SHOVELL, WAS WASHED ASHORE AFTER HIS FLAGSHIP. HMS ASSOCIATION WAS WRECKED ON THE GILSTONE ROCKS ON THE NIGHT OF 22ND OCTOBER 1707

Typical flowers on the islands.

ALPHANUMERICAL INDEX by PORT LETTER NUMBER

	No.	Name	Type	Port		No.	Name	Type	Port
p	FH529	KINGFISHER II	Netter/Potter	CADGWITH	p	FY9	BREEZE	Liner	MEVAGISSEY
p	FH598	GIRL RACHAEL	Trawler	FALMOUTH	p	FY10	CELTIC DAWN	Ring Netter	MEVAGISSEY
p	FH609	DOMAR (Ex M609)	Potter	FALMOUTH	p	FY11	TORRI GWYNT	Liner	NEWLYN
p	FH610	SEA LASS (Ex SC1)	Liner	NEWLYN	p	FY12	OCEAN HARVEST	Trawler	MEVAGISSEY
p	FH613	KERANY (Ex M613)	Liner	PORTHOUSTOCK	p	FY14	SHAKIRA	Netter/Potter/Liner	GORRAN HAVEN
p	FH623	BENEDICTION	Netter/Potter	NEWLYN	p	FY15	FOUR MAIDENS	Tender	MEVAGISSEY
p	FH629	KATHRYN LOUISE II	Netter	THE LIZARD	p	FY17	KINGFISHER of LOOE	Trawler	MEVAGISSEY
	FH638	ELA-J		FALMOUTH	p	FY19	CHRISTINE	Liner	MEVAGISSEY
p	FH664	AMETHYST	Scalloper	FALMOUTH	p	FY23	LITTLE PEARL	Netter	NEWLYN
p	FH665	REBECCA	Scalloper	FALMOUTH	p	FY24	ELLA	Trawler	LOOE
p	FH669	MARIA 2	Netter	FALMOUTH	p	FY26	OCEAN QUEEN	Netter	POLPERRO
p	FH690	PETER JOHN II	Netter	FALMOUTH	p	FY35	OUR MAXINE	Not Registered	RIVER TAMAR
p	FH691	BOB WINNIE	Netter/Potter	CADGWITH	p	FY37	OUR GIRLS (Ex PZ682)	Liner	LOOE
p	FH693	LIZY	Netter	MEVAGISSEY	p	FY38	MAXINE'S PRIDE	To Plymouth	LOOE
p	FH699	SUNSHINE	Liner	COVERACK	p	FY43	LENTEN ROSE	Trawler	MEVAGISSEY
p	FH702	CORNISH LASS	Liner	FALMOUTH	p	FY46	INNISFALLEN	Trawler	NEWLYN
p	FH704	RUBEN LUKE	Netter/Liner	NEWLYN	p	FY47	OUR LIZ	Netter	ST IVES
p	FH705	HOBBIT	Netter	FALMOUTH	p	FY52	C.J		MEVAGISSEY
p	FH706	VICTORIA ANN	Netter	CADGWITH	p	FY53	DEMELZA	Netter	MEVAGISSEY
p	FH714	FRANCES B	Potter	FALMOUTH	p	FY58	VENUS	Netter	MEVAGISSEY
p	FH715	KIMBERLEY JO	Netter/Liner	MEVAGISSEY	p	FY59	SWALLOW	Angler	LOOE
p	FH717	CORNISH LASS IV	Potter	COVERACK	p	FY66	LUCY TOO	Netter	LOOE
p	FH722	PROPHET	Potter	FALMOUTH	p	FY81	RUBY	Liner	MEVAGISSEY
p	FH723	HARVESTER II	Netter/Potter	FALMOUTH	p	FY83	ELISABETH VERONIQUE	Trawler	NEWLYN
p	FH728	STERENNYK	Netter/Liner	HELFORD RIVER	p	FY88	BUCCANEER	Netter	MEVAGISSEY
p	FH733	FLOWER OF FAL		FALMOUTH	p	FY91	MANX RANGER	Trawler/Scalloper	MEVAGISSEY
p	FH734	PATRICIA ANNE	Potter	FALMOUTH	p	FY96	AQUAMANDA	Netter	FALMOUTH
p	FH735	SWEET TART	Not Registered	PORTHLEVEN	p	FY97	GALATEA	Trawler	LOOE
p	FH740	REBECCA TOO	Netter	FALMOUTH	p	FY108	TRUST (Ex PD108)	Liner	MEVAGISSEY
p	FH744	MINSTREL	Netter/Liner	COVERACK	p	FY111	RED VIXEN	Netter/Potter	MEVAGISSEY
p	FH745	MORVRAN	Liner	FALMOUTH	p	FY119	RESOLUTE	Ring Netter	NEWLYN
p	FH746	MILLY II	Net/Pot/Liner	COVERACK	p	FY120	SIRENE	Netter	LOOE
p	FH748	SAPPHIRE	Angler	FALMOUTH	p	FY123	OHIO (SA1238)	Angler	LOOE
p	FH750	MYGHAL	Netter/Potter	NEWLYN	p	FY124	KATYTU (Ex SA1240)	Netter	LOOE
p	FH756	EMILY JAYNE	Netter	HELFORD RIVER	p	FY167	CORAL REEF	Netter	PORTHLEVEN
p	FY1	THREE JAYS	Netter/Potter	GORRAN HAVEN	p	FY174	EMBLEM	Liner	GORRAN HAVEN
p	FY2	MEER	Netter/Liner	LOOE	p	FY180	KATIE LIL	Potter	PORTLOE
p	FY5	FRAYER JAE	Liner	LOOE	p	FY201	IBIS	Netter/Liner	MEVAGISSEY
p	FY6	DOWNDERRY MAID	Liner	LOOE	p	FY222	FREDDIE B	Liner	MEVAGISSEY
p	FY7	LITTLE MO	Liner	RIVER TAMAR	p	FY228	ORCA	Potter	LOOE
p	FY8	SEA SPRAY	Liner	MEVAGISSEY	p	FY278	PUFFIN	Trawler/Liner	MEVAGISSEY

=

ALPHANUMERICAL INDEX by PORT LETTER NUMBER

	Port Letter No.	Name	Type	Port
p	FY 303	DISPATCHER	Crabber	LOOE
p	FY 324	AQUILA	Netter/Potter	MEVAGISSEY
p	FY 332	TAMARA	Netter/Liner	MEVAGISSEY
p	FY 345	LIVER BIRD	Netter	MEVAGISSEY
p	FY 368	MAJESTIC	Potter/Liner	MEVAGISSEY
p	FY 369	PARAVEL	Trawler	LOOE
p	FY 399	BLUE MARLIN	Netter	FOWEY
p	FY 400	MAKO	Liner	MEVAGISSEY
p	FY 431	LIBERTY	Netter/Liner/Angler	MEVAGISSEY
p	FY 470	IMOGEN (Ex PZ100)	Trawler	MEVAGISSEY
p	FY 509	SUPERB II	Netter	MEVAGISSEY
p	FY 523	MORDROS	Netter	LOOE
p	FY 529	VESTA	Potter	PADSTOW
p	FY 545	JENNY JAMES	Netter	GORRAN HAVEN
p	FY 555	LYONESSE	Potter	MEVAGISSEY
p	FY 570	SILVERY SEA	Netter	NEWLYN
p	FY 583	NORTHERN STAR II	Netter	POLPERRO
p	FY 588	BOY JOE II	Liner	MEVAGISSEY
p	FY 602	NATALIE	Trawler	LOOE
p	FY 606	VESPER II(Ex M606)	Netter	MEVAGISSEY
p	FY 614	CAZADORA	Trawler	POLPERRO
p	FY 755	GIRL AMANDA	Netter	MEVAGISSEY
p	FY 759	SURPRISE	Netter	MEVAGISSEY
p	FY 765	LITTLE ANNE	Liner	NEWLYN
	FY 767	NEPTUNE'S PRIDE II	Liner	LOOE
	FY 776	TREWARTHA	Potter	PADSTOW
p	FY 777	FLYING SPRAY IV	Potter	CHARLESTOWN
p	FY 778	TANEGAN (Ex LA778)	Potter	LOOE
p	FY 787	GRANDAD	Liner	HAYLE
p	FY 803	VERONA (Ex WAVE II)	Liner	MEVAGISSEY
p	FY 804	PHOENIX	Netter/Crabber	LOOE
p	FY 807	JESSICA GRACE	Trawler	FOWEY
p	FY 811	MARY EILEEN	Liner	MEVAGISSEY
p	FY 817	SAMMY JAYNE	Potter	MEVAGISSEY
p	FY 822	FAIR WIND	Netter	POLPERRO
p	FY 823	CONWAY	Liner	MEVAGISSEY
p	FY 826	SUNSHINE	Netter/Liner	MEVAGISSEY
p	FY830	ATLANTIS	Trawler/Scalloper	LOOE
p	FY834	KATIE'S PRIDE	Potter	CHARLESTOWN
p	FY836	LAUREN KATE	Netter	MEVAGISSEY
p	FY838	BOY'S OWN II	Liner	LOOE
p	FY841	DEMPER	Netter	MEVAGISSEY
p	FY842	JACOB	Tender	MEVAGISSEY
p	FY843	LUCY B	Netter	MEVAGISSEY
p	FY850	TYPHOON	Netter/Liner/Angler	LOOE
p	FY860	CORNISH LASS	Potter	FOWEY
p	FY868	CORNISHMAN	Netter/Liner	MEVAGISSEY
p	FY869	MYSTIQUE II	Netter/liner/Angler	MOUSEHOLE
p	FY872	MORGELLAN	Liner	MEVAGISSEY
p	FY875	CRIMSON TIDE	Netter	MEVAGISSEY
p	FY881	PETREL	Liner	MEVAGISSEY
p	FY884	TIMMY HAM	Dive Boat	CHARLESTOWN
p	FY886	AVOCET	Liner	MEVAGISSEY
p	FY887	PROVIDENCE	Liner	PAR
p	FY888	PAMELA JANE	Liner	PAR
p	FY889	SCAVENGER	Shellfish dredger	PAR
p	FY890	MOLLY MAI	Liner	MEVAGISSEY
p	FY892	TAMAHINE	Liner	LOOE
p	FY894	HALCYON	Netter/Liner	LOOE
p	FY898	MOOGIE	Angler	LOOE
p	FY903	GUNGIR	Liner	LOOE
p	FY906	BLUE JAY	Liner	FOWEY
p	FY913	MARY ANN	Liner	MEVAGISSEY
p	FY917	BLUE MIST	Angler	LOOE
p	FY918	PANIA (ExSA1239)	Angler	LOOE
p	FY920	JO JO LOUISE	Liner	LOOE
p	FY922	JUBILEE BELLE	Liner	LOOE
p	GY8	PROVIDER	Potter	NEWQUAY
p	GY356	PANDION	Trawler	NEWLYN
p	H22	SPURN LIGHT (Ex M21)	Liner	LOOE
p	H145	SWIFT	Potter	HAYLE
p	HL1059	CYCLONE	Netter	NEWQUAY
p	HL125	BONNY LASS	Potter	HELFORD RIVER
p	LI559	PEPSI	Liner	FOWEY
p	LL307	EARLY DAWN	Potter/Liner	PORTREATH
p	LO540	BANANA SPLIT	Liner	PORTHOUSTOCK
p	LT61	SEA SPRAY	Netter	NEWLYN
p	M99	PROVIDER	Potter	PADSTOW
p	NN18	QUANTUS	Netter/Potter	NEWQUAY

=

ALPHANUMERICAL INDEX by PORT LETTER NUMBER

	No.	Name	Type	Port
p	NN27	BONNIE GRACE	Netter	HELFORD RIVER
p	NN95	CHRISANN	Netter	PORTHLEVEN
p	NN135	BREAKING DAWN	Trawl/Net/Potter	MEVAGISSEY
p	NN137	JOANNA	Trawler	LOOE
p	NN722	GUIDING LIGHT II	To Bideford	LOOE
p	P17	KASTEL PAOL	Potter	NEWLYN
p	P940	DAWN RAIDER	Netter	POLPERRO
P	PE474	KAREN	Trawler/Scalloper	POLPERRO
p	PH25	SULA BASSANA	Net/Potter/Liner	RIVER TAMAR
p	PH307	SPLENDOUR	Potter	RIVER TAMAR
p	PH356	SCATHMAS	Potter	PORTWRINKLE
p	PH572	MY GIRLS	Netter/Potter	POLPERRO
p	PH584	MAID of KENT	Liner	LOOE
p	PH585	SHIRALEE	Potter/Crabber	RIVER TAMAR
p	PH601	CAWSAND BAY	Netter/Potter	LOOE
p	PH959	RICHARD ANN	Netter	MEVAGISSEY
p	PH5547	OUR ROSEANNE	Scalloper	FOWEY
p	PL26	CHRIS TACHA	Trawler	NEWLYN
p	PW1	BERLEWEN	Netter	PADSTOW
p	PW3	SPARKLING LINE	Netter	NEWLYN
p	PW5	HELEN CLAIRE	Potter	PORT ISAAC
p	PW6	SHANMAR	Liner	PADSTOW
p	PW11	CORNISH ROSE	Liner	PADSTOW
p	PW14	Maid of Bodinnick	Crabber	PADSTOW
p	PW15	GIRL SHARON	Potter	PADSTOW
p	PW16	TIZZARDLEE-ON	Netter/Potter	NEWQUAY
p	PW17	GAL CADORA	Potter	NEWQUAY
p	PW20	JANICE MARY	Angler	PORT ISAAC
p	PW21	CELTIC BREEZE	Potter	PADSTOW
p	PW22	GOOD INTENT	Potter	NEWQUAY
p	PW23	SARAFINE	Netter/Potter	SCILLY
p	PW24	OUR KATY	Potter	PADSTOW
p	PW27	PROVIDER	Potter	PADSTOW
p	PW28	OUR ZOE	Potter	PADSTOW
p	PW30	MISTY BLUE	Liner	PADSTOW
p	PW33	DIANA MARION	Liner	NEWLYN
p	PW41	BLACK PEARL	Potter	BUDE
p	PW43	TWILIGHT (	Potter/	BUDE
p	PW44	ELLEN MARY	Potter	BUDE
p	PW45	CHARISMA	Netter/Tuna Liner	PADSTOW
p	PW46	ROAMS	Potter	PADSTOW
p	PW56	DARING	Potter	PORT QUIN
p	PW72	BOY REGGIE	Liner	PADSTOW
p	PW75	PALORES	Netter	POLPERRO
p	PW77	GIRL RACHEL	Netter/Liner	PADSTOW
p	PW81	JULIE GIRL	Netter/Liner	HELFORD RIVER
p	PW95	ELEANOR ROGET	Potter	PADSTOW
p	PW100	OUR BELLE ANN	Potter	PORT ISAAC
p	PW104	SHARICMAR	Potter	PORT ISAAC
p	PW122	ZARVAN	Netter/Potter	NEWQUAY
p	PW124	HELEN JANE II	Netter	PADSTOW
p	PW132	HOMARUS	Potter	PADSTOW
p	PW156	SERENE DAWN	Netter	NEWLYN
p	PW163	FREE SPIRIT	Potter	PORT ISAAC
p	PW177	HARVEST REAPER	Netter	NEWLYN
p	PW214	THOMAS ANDREW	Netter	PADSTOW
p	PW228	MA-VIE	Netter	HELFORD RIVER
p	PW235	BOY JOHN II	Potter	PORT ISAAC
p	PW240	DILIGENCE	Netter/Potter	MEVAGISSEY
p	PW242	OUR WINNIE	Potter	PORT ISAAC
p	PW289	BOSCASTLE PEGANINA	Potter	NEWQUAY
p	PW333	DAYMER BAY	Netter/Potter	PADSTOW
p	PW346	SEA STAR	Liner	NEWLYN
p	PW362	CHARLOTTA	Scalloper/Netter	MEVAGISSEY
p	PW364	ORCADES II	Potter	PORT ISAAC
p	PW392	ERINDORS	Netter	PADSTOW
p	PW445	FALCON	Liner	PADSTOW
p	PW456	LILY MAY II	Potter	BUDE
p	PW458	ORIENT	Trawl/Scalloper	PADSTOW
p	PW460	BLUE FOX	Angler	PADSTOW
p	PW469	For a Few Dollars More	Liner	HAYLE
p	PW473	VIDDY	Liner	LOOE
p	PW474	JACQUELINE	Angler	PADSTOW
p	PW479	ANN KATHLEEN	Potter	NEWLYN
p	PW485	SPINDRIFT	Angler	PADSTOW
p	PZ1	SARAH BETH	Netter/Potter	NEWLYN
p	PZ2	J.S.W	Liner	BOAT COVE
p	PZ4	CORMORAN	Netter	NEWLYN
p	PZ5	SOU'WESTER	Liner	NEWLYN
p	PZ6	GIRL PAMELA	Netter	NEWLYN
p	PZ7	PORTHENYS	Liner	NEWLYN
p	PZ9	MORNING STAR	Netter	PORTHLEVEN
p	PZ10	KAREN N (Ex Nellie)	Scalloper	NEWLYN

IV

V

ALPHANUMERICAL INDEX by PORT LETTER NUMBER

ALPHANUMERICAL INDEX by PORT LETTER NUMBER

p	PZ1209	ROSE BUD	Potter/Liner	SENNEN COVE		p	SS3	GUIDE ME	Liner	LOOE
p	PZ1218	SARAH STEVE	Potter/Angler	NEWLYN		p	SS5	KLONDYKE	Liner	MEVAGISSEY
p	PZ1228	TRENOW GIRL	Liner	NEWLYN		p	SS6	MOLLIE DAWN	Liner	ST IVES
p	PZ1247	LADY JACQUELINE	Liner	NEWLYN		p	SS7	DIANA	Liner	SENNEN COVE
p	R159	MARET	Trawler	LOOE		p	SS8	ASPER	Netter/Liner	ST IVES
p	SC1	TORRIBEE	Liner	NEWLYN		p	SS9	CADOR	Liner	BOAT COVE
p	SC2	LOWENA	Potter/Liner	NEWLYN		p	SS10	GIRL CHERRY	Liner	ST IVES
p	SC4	ROCKHOPPER	Potter	SCILLY		p	SS16	MY ROSS MIST	Potter/Liner	HAYLE
	SC5	SUMMERTIME BLUES		NEWLYN		p	SS17	OSPREY	Netter	ST IVES
p	SC7	HAPPY HOOKER	Liner	NEWLYN		p	SS19	RIPPLE	Lugger	NEWLYN
p	SC8	DANMARK	Trawler	NEWLYN		p	SS21	TIGER	Liner	NEWLYN
p	SC11	VICTORY of Helford	Trawler	SCILLY		p	SS22	INSPIRATION	Liner	NEWLYN
p	SC14	STAR of the NORTH	Netter/Potter	NEWLYN		p	SS24	JODA	Liner	HAYLE
p	SC16	NORTHERN STAR	Liner/Potter	SCILLY		p	SS25	KELLY GIRL	Liner	ST IVES
p	SC17	ATLANTIS	Liner/Potter	SCILLY		p	SS28	LAMORNA	Netter	NEWLYN
p	SC19	FORGET-ME-NOT	Netter	MOUSEHOLE		p	SS30	ROSEBUD	Liner	NEWLYN
p	SC21	NAZARENE	Liner	NEWLYN		p	SS32	SEA BREEZE	Net/Pot/Liner	HAYLE
p	SC25	NORTHWOOD	Liner	NEWLYN		p	SS33	WHITE HEATHER	Netter	NEWLYN
p	SC27	ISIS	Netter	MEVAGISSEY		p	SS35	MAGGIE	Liner	ST IVES
p	SC32	VICKY ANNA	Netter/Potter	SCILLY		p	SS40	TOLLBAR	Liner	NEWQUAY
p	SC35	EMERALD DAWN	Potter	SCILLY		p	SS41	SANDPIPER	Liner	ST IVES
p	SC41	PIONEER	Netter/Potter	SCILLY		p	SS45	SHANNON	Netter/Potter	NEWQUAY
p	SC50	ZEPHYR	Liner	NEWLYN		p	SS46	MARY MO	Liner	ST IVES
p	SC60	LEONORA	Netter/Liner	MEVAGISSEY		p	SS53	NORAH-T	Liner	ST IVES
p	SC70	CURLEW	Netter	SCILLY		p	SS61	KEIRA	Liner	ST IVES
p	SC73	STEREN-MOR	Netter	MEVAGISSEY		p	SS65	HOPE	Liner	NEWLYN
p	SC76	PELICAN	Potter	SCILLY		p	SS66	PHRA - NANG	Potter	HAYLE
p	SC167	MAIDEN BOWER	Potter	SCILLY		p	SS67	TRACEY CLARE	Netter	HELFORD RIVER
p	SC168	BOY ADAM	Potter	SCILLY		p	SS76	TILLERMAN	Liner	NEWLYN
p	SC172	PONTIOUS	Potter	SCILLY		p	SS80	LITTLE CHRISTINA	Netter/Liner	ST IVES
p	SC173	RESOLUTION	Netter/Potter	SCILLY		p	SS87	PRIDE OF CORNWALL	Ring Netter	NEWLYN
p	SC175	MARAUDER	Trawler	SCILLY		p	SS88	TEGEN MOR	Net/Pot/Liner	HAYLE
p	SC177	GALLOS	Netter/Potter	SCILLY		p	SS92	ELISHIA	Netter/Liner	NEWLYN
p	SC181	SOWENNA	Netter	NEWLYN		p	SS118	CRYSTAL SEA	Twin Rig Trawler	NEWLYN
p	SD201	NEPTUNE	Trawl/Scalloper	NEWLYN		p	SS120	BOTE	Potter	ST AGNES
p	SD383	FREEDOM	Trawler	RIVER TAMAR		p	SS126	NIKKI LOUISE	Netter	NEWLYN
p	SE10	BLUE PLOVER	Potter	HAYLE		p	SS136	CYNTHIA	Liner	NEWLYN
p	SM300	PEDRO	Liner	LOOE		p	SS138	PETER PAN	Liner	NEWLYN
p	SN4	BOLD VENTURE	Potter	PORTHOUSTOCK		p	SS144	JANET ANNE	Netter	NEWLYN
p	SS1	BOY JAKE	Liner	ST IVES		p	SS149	MARANATHA	Potter	SCILLY
p	SS2	BLUE BELLE	Liner	ST IVES						

ALPHANUMERICAL INDEX by PORT LETTER NUMBER

p	SS151	HAWK	Liner	MOUSEHOLE
p	SS161	DIGNITY	Netter/Liner	ST IVES
p	SS170	JEN	Liner	ST IVES
p	SS173	RHIANNON JANE	Netter	MEVAGISSEY
p	SS209	STILL WATERS	Potter/liner	ST IVES
p	SS224	MARINER	Netter	ST IVES
p	SS225	AGAN PROVIYAS	Potter	ST IVES
p	SS226	DAPHNE ROSE	Liner	SENNEN COVE
p	SS233	TRYPHENA	Liner	MEVAGISSEY
p	SS233	TRYPHENA	Liner	NEWQUAY
p	SS247	WINKLE	Potter/liner	ST AGNES
p	SS252	BETHSHAN	Liner	NEWLYN
p	SS258	TUDOR ROSE	Liner	PORTHLEVEN
p	SS261	AMMO	Netter	ST IVES
p	SS262	ANNA MARIA	Potter/Liner	HAYLE
p	SS266	BELLE BETTINA	Netter	ST IVES
P	SS268	RAZORBILL	Netter	CADGWITH
p	SS270	ZARA	Liner	MEVAGISSEY
p	SS273	ORION	Netter/Liner	MOUSEHOLE
p	SS276	BOY CHRIS	Liner	NEWLYN
p	SS324	BRODI SEA	Netter/Liner	HAYLE
p	SS665	BRISSONS	Liner	ST IVES
p	SS673	MAID MEL	Netter/Liner	HAYLE
p	SS681	LADY JOAN	Liner	ST IVES
p	SS683	MARLIN G	Netter/Liner	MEVAGISSEY
p	SS694	MIDGE	Liner	MOUSEHOLE
p	SS697	ELLE V	Netter/Liner	HAYLE
p	SS707	ORCA	Potter	HAYLE
p	SS710	SALLY	Liner/Angler	ST IVES
p	SS711	BONITO	Liner	HAYLE
p	SS713	LYONESS	Liner	ST IVES
p	SS716	SHIKARI	Liner	NEWLYN
p	SS717	BOY DANIEL		NEWLYN
p	SS723	SIR JACK		NEWLYN
p	SS738	PROPER JOB	Liner	HAYLE
p	SS739	AUTUMN SILVER	Liner	NEWLYN
p	SS744	SEA MAIDEN	Liner	HAYLE
p	SS748	RAVEN	Liner	NEWLYN
p	SS759	MAXINE CHARLOTTE	Liner	FALMOUTH
p	ST5	DREAM CATCHER	Liner	NEWLYN
p	SU13	CHALLENGE	Trawler/Scalloper	MEVAGISSEY

p	SU514	HOPE	Trawler	POLPERRO
p	TH177	ICTHUS	Potter	PADSTOW
p	TH288	GOLDEN LANCER	Netter/Potter	NEWQUAY
p	TH424	KAY-LARIE	Netter	SCILLY
p	TN35	OLIVIA JEAN	Beam Trawler	NEWLYN
p	TO5	MARINA II	Liner	NEWLYN
p	TO6	ALANA TROY	Liner	MEVAGISSEY
p	TO7	COSMO'S MARINER	Netter/Liner	PORTREATH
p	TO10	SARAH JANE	Potter	ST AGNES
p	TO32	AJAX	Netter	NEWLYN
p	TO40	INTUITION	Potter	NEWLYN
p	TO41	BOY RYAN	Liner	NEWLYN
p	TO46	SHAMROCK	Netter	PADSTOW
p	TO48	GOOD FORTUNE	Potter	PORTREATH
p	TO60	EMMA LOUISE	Potter	NEWLYN
p	WH6	CHERYL ANN	Liner	LOOE
p	WH97	DRAGUM-AN-MOAR	Liner	NEWLYN
p	WH111	BETHANY J	Potter	PADSTOW
p	WH264	PROSPECTOR	Potter	NEWLYN
p	WH324	LIKELY LAD	Potter	MEVAGISSEY
p	WH578	BOY BRAX	Netter/Liner	NEWLYN
p	WH606	LITTLE LAUREN	Liner	SCILLY
p	WK3	BEN LOYAL	Tuna Liner	NEWLYN
p	WY160	LEON	Potter	NEWLYN
p	WY830	CHUTNEY	Liner	ST AGNES
p	YH199	MARY D	Potter	PORT ISAAC
p	YH563	HIGHLIGHT	Potter	PORT GAVERNE
p	YH2489	HAPPY DAYS	Potter	BUDE

VIII

ALPHABETICAL INDEX by NAME

	Reg	Name	Length	Port
p	SN34	BOLD VENTURE	5.91	PORTHOUSTOCK
p	BM367	BON ACCORD	14.9	LOOE
p	TN104	BON AMY (Ex PW470)	8.25	PADSTOW
p	SS711	BONITO	7.2	ST IVES
p	NN27	BONNIE GRACE	7.74	HELFORD RIVER
p	HL125	BONNY LASS	6.4	HELFORD RIVER
p	PW289	BOSCASTLE PEGANINA	9.31	NEWQUAY
p	SS120	BOTE	4.27	ST AGNES
p	PZ302	BOY ADAM	5.86	NEWLYN
p	SC168	BOY ADAM	4.73	SCILLY
p	Ex M597	BOY BRAD (Ex FH657)	4.8	PORTHALLOW
p	WH578	BOY BRAX (Ex AMRO)	5.6	NEWLYN
p	SS276	BOY CHRIS	4.74	NEWLYN
p	P295	BOY CODY	5.6	PORTHLEVEN
p	Ex FH614	BOY DANIEL	4.4	NEWLYN
p	SS717	BOY DANIEL	5.5	NEWLYN
p	Ex PZ224	BOY DANNY	6.5	NEWLYN
p	BS422	BOY DARREN	6.4	NEWQUAY
p	PZ11	BOY DYLAN	5.8	NEWLYN
p	Ex PZ11	BOY DYLAN	5.8	MOUSEHOLE
p	Ex PZ824	BOY GABRIEL	7.92	PENZANCE
p	PZ379	BOY HARVEY	7.7	HAYLE
p	SS1	BOY JAKE	4.83	ST IVES
p	PZ1197	BOY JAMES	5.38	PORTHLEVEN
p	FY588	BOY JOE II	4.8	MEVAGISSEY
p	PW235	BOY JOHN II	5.33	PORT ISAAC
p	PZ699	BOY MATT	4.9	SENNEN COVE
p	PW72	BOY REGGIE	4.2	PADSTOW
p	TO41	BOY RYAN	4.78	NEWLYN
p	FY764	BOY WILLIAM	6.32	POLPERRO
p	FY838	BOY'S OWN II	6	LOOE
p	NN135	BREAKING DAWN	9.6	MEVAGISSEY
p	FY9	BREEZE	5.2	MEVAGISSEY
p	SS665	BRISSONS	4.8	ST IVES
p	FH508	Britannia IV of Falmouth	10	NEWLYN
p	FH121	BRITANNIA V	15.5	NEWLYN
p	SS324	BRODI SEA	9.2	HAYLE
p	FY88	BUCCANEER	8.4	MEVAGISSEY
p	PZ584	BUTTS	5.73	MOUSEHOLE

	Reg	Name	Length	Port
p	FY52	C.J.	6.6	NEWLYN
p	Ex PZ1201	CACHALOT	5.4	NEWLYN
p	SS9	CADOR	6.81	FALMOUTH
p	Ex SS54	CALIOPE	10.1	PADSTOW
p	PZ15	CAPRIOLE	15	NEWLYN
p	PZ715	CARES LEL	5.6	NEWLYN
p	FH89	CARIAD	29.9	NEWLYN
p	PZ17	CARISSA ANN	22.5	NEWLYN
p	PZ2620	CAROL & DAVID	4.5	NEWLYN
p	Ex WY379	CAROL H	5.4	BUDE
p	SE322	CARPE DIEM	6.7	NEWLYN
p	Ex FH610	CATHERINE ANNE	4.6	GORRAN HAVEN
p	PZ232	CATHRYN	8.8	PADSTOW
p	PH601	CAWSAND BAY (Ex FH&PT601)	16.4	NEWLYN
p	FY614	CAZADORA	25.3	NEWLYN
p	FH6	CELESTIAL DAWN	7.47	NEWLYN
p	PZ557	CELTIC BREEZE	7.3	PORTHLEVEN
p	PW21	CELTIC BREEZE (Ex AB214)	5.13	PADSTOW
p	FY10	CELTIC DAWN (Ex WK10)	6.25	COVERACK
p	PZ1200	CELTIC SUNRISE	5.9	NEWLYN
p	Ex PZ184	CERES	24.8	NEWLYN
p	BD279	CERI LEE	4.81	PADSTOW
p	Ex TO50	CESCA (Ex FR1 Accord)	26.3	NEWLYN
p	SU513	CHALLENGE	9.33	FALMOUTH
p	Ex SE70	CHANCE	5.49	FALMOUTH
p	Ex LK50	CHANTELLE	5.55	MULLION COVE
p	SM799	CHARELLA of Shoreham	6.19	COVERACK
p	SS11	CHARISMA	8.13	CHARLESTOWN
p	PW45	CHARISMA (Ex BA45)	4.3	MEVAGISSEY
p	SU515	CHARITY & LIBERTY	4.3	MEVAGISSEY
p	PW362	CHARLOTTA	4.74	COVERACK
p	Ex FY156	CHARM	5.6	MEVAGISSEY
p	Ex PW432	CHE SARA SARA	6.06	MEVAGISSEY
p	Ex WH6	CHERYL ANN	9.95	PORT ISAAC
p	PZ282	CHICADEE	8.5	PORT ISAAC
p	Ex SS704	CHLOE ESTELLE	5.52	NEWLYN
p	Ex PZ1186	CHLOE T (Ex BM190)	4.9	GORRAN HAVEN
p	NN95	CHRISANN	5.85	CADGWITH
p	FY19	CHRISTINE	11.9	MEVAGISSEY

X

ALPHABETICAL INDEX by NAME

XII

ALPHABETICAL INDEX by NAME

p	PZ329	HARVEST REAPER	11.9	NEWLYN
p	PW177	HARVEST REAPER (Ex TT177)	17	NEWLYN
p	FH723	HARVESTER II	11.8	FALMOUTH
p	SS151	HAWK	5.6	MOUSEHOLE
p	Ex FY126	HEATHER ANNE	11	MEVAGISSEY
p	PW5	HELEN CLAIRE	9.66	PORT ISAAC
p	Ex PW429	HELEN CLARE II	10	PORT ISAAC
p	M1103	HELEN D	5.9	ST IVES
p	Ex PW412	HELEN JANE	9.65	NEWQUAY
p	PW124	HELEN JANE II	9.8	PADSTOW
p	PZ682	HELONA	5.75	NEWQUAY
p	PZ654	HICCA	4.8	PENBERTH
p	YH563	HIGHLIGHT	4.91	PORT GAVERNE
p	FH705	HOBBIT	5.88	FALMOUTH
p	PW132	HOMARUS	7.8	PADSTOW
p	SS65	HOPE	6.05	NEWLYN
p	Ex SS65	HOPE	4.7	ST IVES
p	SU514	HOPE	12	POLPERRO
p	Ex PZ787	HOUR OFF	6.75	NEWLYN
p	Ex FY424	HUNTRESS	8.7	MEVAGISSEY
p	FY201	IBIS	5.9	MEVAGISSEY
p	TH177	ICTHUS	12.2	PADSTOW
p	FH93	IDA MAY	4.5	THE LIZARD
p	Ex PZ213	I'LL TRY	5.5	HELFORD RIVER
p	FY470	IMOGEN (Ex PZ100)	10.4	MEVAGISSEY
p	PZ110	IMOGEN II (Ex OB15)	12	NEWLYN
	Ex PZ110	IMOGEN II (Ex KY202)	14	NEWLYN
p	M3	INDUSTRIOUS	9.98	BOSCASTLE
p	FY46	INNISFALLEN	10	NEWLYN
p	SS22	INSPIRATION	5.6	NEWLYN
p	TO40	INTUITION	18	NEWLYN
p	FY367	INVESTOR	9.75	MEVAGISSEY
p	FH23	IONA	4.5	PORTSCATHO
p	SC27	ISIS	7.6	MEVAGISSEY
p	CN119	ISLANDER	6.21	MOUSEHOLE
p	Ex FY296	ISLANDER	6.6	POLPERRO
p	PZ2	J.S.W	4.45	BOAT COVE
p	BD57	JACAMAR	8.57	NEWLYN

p	Ex PZ779	JACK-ANNY	4.68	NEWLYN
p	PZ495	JACKIE MARIE	5.6	MEVAGISSEY
p	FY842	JACOB	3.86	MEVAGISSEY
p	PZ307	JACOBA (Ex UK307)	37	NEWLYN
p	PW474	JACQUELINE	6.78	PADSTOW
p	FH729	JACQUELINE ANNE	10.9	FALMOUTH
p	PZ695	JADE	5.9	HAYLE
p	PZ78	JAMES R.H. STEVENSON	29.8	NEWLYN
p	FH353	JANE LOUISE	7.75	LOOE
p	SS144	JANET ANNE	5.6	NEWLYN
p	PW20	JANICE MARY	6	PORT ISAAC
p	Ex PZ19	J-ANNE (Ex BRD92)	8.93	NEWLYN
p	Ex PZ999	JANNIE EN KLAAS	26.2	NEWLYN
p	FH75	JASMINE	5	PORTLOE
p	Ex FH14	JASPER	5.42	NEWLYN
p	Ex PZ818	JAY JAY	4.9	NEWLYN
p	SS170	JEN	4.9	ST IVES
p	FH200	JEN-LOU II	5	PORTHOUSTOCK
p	Ex LL272	JENNA LEA	13	PAR
p	PZ20	JENNY	4.69	NEWLYN
	FY545	JENNY JAMES	3.8	GORRAN HAVEN
p	FY807	JESSICA GRACE	9	MEVAGISSEY
p	FY807	JESSICA GRACE	9.7	FOWEY
p	Ex FY837	JIMINI K	3.9	MEVAGISSEY
p	NN137	JOANNA	14	LOOE
p	SS24	JODA	6	HAYLE
p	PZ689	JOHN LOUISE	4.76	NEWLYN
p	SS284	JOHN WESLEY	11.9	LOOE
p	Ex SS112	JOHNATHAN SEAGULL	5.2	ST IVES
p	FY920	JO JO LOUISE	5.6	LOOE
p	PZ111	JOSEPHINE	5.6	NEWLYN
p	PZ79	JOSH II	5.55	THE LIZARD
p	FY922	JUBLEE BELLE	6	LOOE
p	Ex SS221	JULIA NADINE	4.3	ST IVES
p	PW81	JULIE GIRL	8.15	HELFORD RIVER
p	Ex SC163	KAMERUKA	7.4	SCILLY
p	PE474	KAREN MARIE	9.97	POLPERRO
p	PZ10	KAREN N	22.2	NEWLYN

ALPHABETICAL INDEX by NAME

p	PZ35	KARENZA	(Ex SC170)	6.16	NEWLYN
p	FH88	KARENZA JAYNE		6.62	HELFORD RIVER
p	Ex E20	KARLI-N		8	RIVER TAMAR
p	P1007	KASTEL PAOL		17.4	NEWLYN
p	PZ86	KATHLEEN		6.05	NEWLYN
p	FH629	KATHRYN LOUISE II		4.5	THE LIZARD
p	PZ287	KATIE CLAIRE		13.5	MEVAGISSEY
p	FY180	KATIE LIL		6	PORTLOE
p	FY834	KATIE'S PRIDE		5.5	CHARLESTOWN
p	CS295	KATY		4.4	GORRAN HAVEN
p	PZ18	KATY		4.89	PORTHLEVEN
p	FY124	KATYTU	(Ex SA1240)	6.01	LOOE
p	TH424	KAY-LARIE	(Ex SU414)	6.6	SCILLY
p	SS61	KEIRA		5.75	ST IVES
p	SS25	KELLY GIRL		5.8	ST IVES
p	PZ480	KELYN MOR		4.6	NEWQUAY
p	FH613	KERANY	(Ex M613)	4.75	PORTHOUSTOCK
p	Ex FY63	KERRY JAYNE		9.1	MEVAGISSEY
p	FH715	KIMBERLEY JO		6.53	MEVAGISSEY
p	BK524	KINDLY LIGHT D		7.45	COVERACK
p	Ex FH529	KINGFISHER II		7.77	CADGWITH
p	FH529	KINGFISHER II		7.62	CADGWITH
p	FY17	KINGFISHER of LOOE		10.3	MEVAGISSEY
p	SS5	KLONDYKE		5.5	MEVAGISSEY
p	FH187	KON-TIKI		4.3	HELFORD RIVER
p	Ex M111	KSH		9.15	RIVER TAMAR
p	Ex PZ436	L'AURORE (Ex Michael & David)		11.1	NEWLYN
p	Ex SS96	LADY ANNE		5.2	ST IVES
p	Ex PW287	LADY DI		6.6	PORTREATH
p	FH214	Lady Hamilton of Helford		8.53	HELFORD RIVER
p	PZ1247	LADY JACQUELINE		6.75	NEWLYN
p	SS681	LADY JOAN		5.7	ST IVES
p	Ex FH726	LADY LYNDA		7.3	HELFORD RIVER
p	FH19	LADY MARGARET		4.9	COVERACK
p	Ex PE888	LADY MATILDA		9.2	HELFORD RIVER
p	PZ21	LADY OF ENNIS		5.86	PORTHLEVEN
p	SS28	LAMORNA		12	NEWLYN
p	Ex PZ272	LAURAN		4.76	NEWLYN
p	FY836	LAUREN KATE		9.95	MEVAGISSEY

p	Ex PZ453	LAURIE JEAN		5.6	MULLION COVE
p	Ex PH600	LE BONHEUR		8.9	FOWEY
p	Ex PW36	LE LOUSTIC		5.9	PADSTOW
p	P298	LEADER		5.5	NEWLYN
p	Ex PW455	LENNY P		4.93	PORT GAVERNE
p	FY43	LENTEN ROSE		9.98	MEVAGISSEY
p	WY160	LEON		9.55	NEWLYN
p	SC60	LEONORA		6.6	MEVAGISSEY
p	Ex FY269	LEVAN MOR of LOOE		10.8	LOOE
p	FH485	LEVIATHAN		9.94	FALMOUTH
p	FY431	LIBERTY		8.1	MEVAGISSEY
p	WH324	LIKELY LAD		9.85	MEVAGISSEY
p	PZ457	LILY		5	MOUSEHOLE
p	BM91	LILY LOLA		7.85	PADSTOW
p	PW456	LILY MAY II		6.9	BUDE
p	TO3	LILY'S PRIDE		6.6	PORTREATH
p	Ex FY781	LINDA B		6.7	NEWLYN
p	PZ395	LISA		6.74	NEWLYN
p	PZ476	Lisa Jacquie STEVENSON		24.2	NEWLYN
p	Ex FY302	LISANNE of LOOE		9.75	LOOE
p	FY765	LITTLE ANNE		4.88	NEWLYN
p	Ex SS80	LITTLE CHRISTINA		7.5	ST IVES
p	SS80	Little CHRISTINA (Ex SS104)		7.8	ST IVES
p	Ex FY29	LITTLE FISHER		8.8	RIVER TAMAR
p	Ex PZ758	LITTLE HALCYON		4.6	MOUSEHOLE
p	PZ14	LITTLE LAUREN		4.87	HELFORD RIVER
p	WH606	LITTLE LAUREN		4.8	SCILLY
p	FY7	LITTLE MO		4.75	RIVER TAMAR
p	FY23	LITTLE PEARL		9.98	NEWLYN
p	Ex PZ890	LITTLE WATERS		11.3	NEWLYN
p	FY345	LIVER BIRD		6.4	MEVAGISSEY
p	FH693	LIZY		9.97	MEVAGISSEY
p	SC169	LORRAINE RUTH		8.28	SCILLY
p	PZ283	LOUELLA		4.45	PADSTOW
p	PZ101	LOUISA N	(Ex BM28)	23.1	NEWLYN
p	SC2	LOWENA		6.9	NEWLYN
p	PZ247	LOWENA - MOR		6	NEWLYN
p	Ex SC178	LOWENDA		9.98	NEWLYN

XIV

ALPHABETICAL INDEX by NAME

	Code	NAME		Port
p	SS53	NORAH-T	5.6	ST IVES
p	SC16	NORTHERN STAR	4.45	SCILLY
p	FY583	NORTHERN STAR II	7.8	POLPERRO
p	SC25	NORTHWOOD	7.47	NEWLYN
p	Ex FY44	NORVIK	7.9	LOOE
p	PZ187	NOVA SPERO (Ex CN187)	20.4	NEWLYN
p	Ex FY857	OCEAN BLUE	9.95	LOOE
p	PZ775	OCEAN BREEZE	5.62	NEWLYN
p	FY12	OCEAN HARVEST (Ex SY5)	11.4	MEVAGISSEY
p	FY26	OCEAN QUEEN	8.3	POLPERRO
p	PZ41	OCEAN SPRAY	14.1	NEWLYN
p	FY123	OHIO (Ex SS689 & SA1238)	5.6	LOOE
p	TN35	OLIVIA JEAN (Ex BM181)	33.9	NEWLYN
p	PZ768	ONWARD	4.73	NEWLYN
p	FY228	ORCA	6.3	LOOE
p	SS707	ORCA	6.9	HAYLE
p	PW364	ORCADES II	12.2	PORT ISAAC
p	PW458	ORIENT	8.4	PADSTOW
p	SS273	ORION	8	MOUSEHOLE
p	SS17	OSPREY	5	ST IVES
p	PZ127	OSPREY (Ex WK127)	9.9	PORTHLEVEN
p	PW100	OUR BELLE ANN	11.7	PORT ISAAC
p	Ex LT1	OUR BOY ANDREW	10	LOOE
p	FY37	OUR GIRLS (Ex PZ682)	5.7	LOOE
p	PZ260	OUR KATIE	7	PORTHLEVEN
p	PW24	OUR KATY	5.6	PADSTOW
p	FY47	OUR LIZ	8.7	ST IVES
p	PZ738	OUR MARGARET	5.57	NEWLYN
p	FY35	OUR MAXINE	4.56	RIVER TAMAR
p	PH5547	OUR ROSEANNE	9.99	FOWEY
p	PW242	OUR WINNIE	3.96	PORT ISAAC
p	PW289	OUR ZOE	7.4	PADSTOW
	PW75	PALORES	7.9	POLPERRO
p	FY888	PAMELA JANE	6.9	PAR
p	Ex PZ21	PANDORA III	4.5	MOUSEHOLE
p	FY918	PANIA (Ex FY960 & SA1239)	6.2	LOOE
p	FY369	PARAVEL	10.9	LOOE
p	AB199	PATHFINDER	8.5	NEWQUAY
p	PZ125	PATRICE	8	PADSTOW

	Code	NAME		Port
p	FH55	PATRICE II	7.78	FALMOUTH
p	FH734	PATRICIA ANNE	5.82	FALMOUTH
p	PZ140	PAUL ARRAN	5.9	ST IVES
p	FH300	PAULA ROSE	7.19	FALMOUTH
p	PZ67	PEDDEN	4.8	HELFORD RIVER
p	SM300	PEDRO	7	LOOE
p	PZ729	PEGASUS	6.42	NEWLYN
p	SC76	PELICAN	4.46	SCILLY
p	PZ84	PEN KERNOW	4.5	CAPE CORNWALL
p	PZ118	PENDOWER (Ex PZ1183)	5.59	MEVAGISSEY
p	Ex SC22	PENGUIN	7.92	SCILLY
p	PZ747	PENNY LYNN	5.6	SENNEN COVE
p	PZ631	PENVER	4.6	PENBERTH
p	LI559	PEPSI	5.52	FOWEY
p	FH5	PERSEVERANCE	12.4	HELFORD RIVER
p	FH690	PETER JOHN II	8.02	FALMOUTH
p	SS138	PETER PAN	5.7	NEWLYN
p	FY881	PETREL	6.25	MEVAGISSEY
p	FY804	PHOENIX	9.98	LOOE
p	SS66	PHRA - NANG	8.3	HAYLE
p	Ex FY797	PIMPERNEL II	4.8	MEVAGISSEY
p	Ex YH1	PIONEER	9.2	NEWQUAY
p	SC41	PIONEER	8.02	SCILLY
p	PZ770	POL PRY II	4.8	SENNEN COVE
p	SC172	PONTIOUS	6.2	SCILLY
p	PZ7	PORTHENYS	5.6	NEWLYN
p	SS87	PRIDE OF CORNWALL	9.9	NEWLYN
p	PZ437	PRINCES ROSE	5.56	NEWLYN
p	SS738	PROPER JOB	6.9	HAYLE
p	Ex FH442	PROPERJOB	4.66	FALMOUTH
p	FH722	PROPHET	6.85	FALMOUTH
p	WH264	PROSPECTOR	9.89	NEWLYN
	FY887	PROVIDENCE	5.85	PAR
	GY18	PROVIDER	5.84	NEWQUAY
	PW27	PROVIDER	11.1	PADSTOW
p	PZ550	PRUE ESTHER II	11.6	NEWLYN
p	FY278	PUFFIN	7.4	MEVAGISSEY
p	NN18	QUANTUS	7.07	NEWQUAY
p	PZ612	RACHEL & PAUL	5.6	NEWLYN

p	Ex PZ2570	RACHEL CARA	4.5	CAPE CORNWALL
p	FY270	RADJEL	6.6	MEVAGISSEY
p	SS748	RAVEN (Ex M748)	4.77	NEWLYN
p	SS268	RAZORBILL	5.6	CADGWITH
p	Ex FH700	REBECCA	4.9	FALMOUTH
p	FH665	REBECCA	9.97	FALMOUTH
p	PZ800	REBECCA ANNE	5.58	NEWLYN
p	FH740	REBECCA TOO	5.75	FALMOUTH
p	FY111	RED VIXEN	10.4	MEVAGISSEY
p	Ex PZ475	RELIANCE	9.3	PORTHLEVEN
p	PZ124	REMY-D	5.12	SENNEN COVE
p	E519	RENE	5.96	BOSCASTLE
p	FY119	RESOLUTE	9.95	NEWLYN
p	Ex UL580	RESOLUTE	5.6	MEVAGISSEY
p	SC173	RESOLUTION	7.95	SCILLY
p	PZ1001	RESURGAM	26.2	NEWLYN
p	Ex SC183	RETARRIER	8.45	NEWLYN
p	PZ520	REWARD	6.5	LOOE
p	Ex PZ76	RHIANNON	6.2	PORTHLEVEN
p	SS173	RHIANNON JANE	5.9	MEVAGISSEY
p	Ex FH8	RHODA MARY	8.38	FALMOUTH
p	PH959	RICHARD ANN	9.99	MEVAGISSEY
p	SS19	RIPPLE	13.4	NEWLYN
p	PW46	ROAMS (Ex PT46 & PW463)	4.84	PADSTOW
p	Ex SA28	ROBBYN (Now WY839)	5.06	MULLION COVE
p	SC4	ROCKHOPPER	4.73	SCILLY
p	PZ638	RO-MI-CHRIS	4.88	NEWLYN
p	FH4	ROSE (Ex FH686)	4.7	PORTSCATHO
p	PZ1209	ROSE BUD	4.88	SENNEN COVE
p	PZ816	ROSE of MOUSEHOLE	5.6	MOUSEHOLE
p	SS30	ROSEBUD	4.72	NEWLYN
p	Ex BD252	ROSEN	8	PAR
p	FH3	ROSEN	6.17	PORTSCATHO
p	Ex PZ1024	ROS-NA-RIOGH	14.5	NEWLYN
p	FY81	RUBY (Ex FY829 & M1188)	4.5	MEVAGISSEY
p	PZ343	RUBY MAE	4.88	BOAT COVE
p	Ex FH716	RUBY TUESDAY	4.61	FALMOUTH
p	FH704	RUEBEN LUKE	6.08	NEWLYN

p	WY335	SAEDIA LOUISE	10.9	HELFORD RIVER
p	Ex SS42	SAFI	5.9	ST IVES
p	Ex DH42	SAINT PETROX	7.77	NEWLYN
p	PZ677	SALAMANDA	6.9	PORTHLEVEN
p	Ex BM502	SALAMANDER	9.5	NEWQUAY
p	SS710	SALLY	6.11	HAYLE
p	PZ1191	SALLY ROSE OF NAVAX	7.3	HAYLE
p	FY817	SAMMY JAYNE	4.8	MEVAGISSEY
p	Ex SC8	SAMSON	7.68	SCILLY
p	Ex FY885	SAMUEL JAMES	6	RIVER TAMAR
p	Ex PW25	SAN MARIA	6.22	BUDE
p	SS41	SANDPIPER	5	ST IVES
p	PZ66	SAPPHIRE	25.1	NEWLYN
p	FH748	SAPPHIRE	6.68	FALMOUTH
p	PZ115	SAPPHIRE II	26.5	NEWLYN
p	Ex PZ123	SARA SHAUN	25.3	NEWLYN
p	PW23	SARAFINE	7.15	SCILLY
p	PZ22	SARAH - M	5.91	NEWLYN
p	Ex PZ545	SARAH ANN	4.88	PENZANCE
p	PZ1	SARAH BETH	8.76	NEWLYN
p	TO10	SARAH JANE	4.93	ST AGNES
p	Ex FH273	SARAH JANE of HELFORD	7.5	HAYLE
p	PZ155	SARAH JANE T	4.6	SENNEN COVE
p	PZ1218	SARAH STEVE	8.01	NEWLYN
p	FH85	SCATH DU	6.8	FALMOUTH
p	PH356	SCATHMAS	4.35	PORTWRINKLE
p	FY889	SCAVENGER	4.12	PAR
p	PZ707	SCORPIO	7.75	CADGWITH
p	SS32	SEA BREEZE	9	HAYLE
p	FH11	SEA FOAM	7.38	COVERACK
p	PZ62	SEA FOX	5.87	NEWLYN
p	CK930	SEA GLORY	6.82	HAYLE
p	PZ1199	SEA GOBLIN	4.85	MOUSEHOLE
p	PZ410	SEA HUNTER	5.2	NEWLYN
p	FH610	SEA LASS (Ex SC1)	5.85	NEWLYN
p	PZ1052	SEA MAIDEN	7.99	HAYLE
p	SS744	SEA MAIDEN	6.8	HAYLE
p	PZ317	SEA SPIRIT	6.5	HAYLE
p	Ex PZ402	SEA SPRAY	5.56	PORTHLEVEN

ALPHABETICAL INDEX by NAME

p	FY8	SEA SPRAY	MEVAGISSEY	4.95
p	LT61	SEA SPRAY	NEWLYN	9.93
p	PW346	SEA STAR	NEWLYN	5.6
p	FH119	SEA URCHIN (Ex M1193)	PORTHALLOW	4.76
p	PW156	SERENE DAWN (Ex OB156)	NEWLYN	11.9
p	FY14	SHAKIRA	GORRAN HAVEN	4.23
p	E524	SHAMROCK	PADSTOW	8
p	TO46	SHAMROCK	PADSTOW	5.95
p	Ex SS40	SHAMROCK	NEWQUAY	5.6
p	PW6	SHANMAR	PADSTOW	5.02
p	SS45	SHANNON	NEWQUAY	9.2
p	PW104	SHARICMAR	PORT ISAAC	8.22
p	Ex PZ590	SHE WOLF	HAYLE	9.9
p	PZ76	SHIELA T	PORTHLEVEN	8.5
p	SS716	SHIKARI	ST IVES	5.7
p	BM35	SHIRALEE	NEWLYN	9.8
p	PH585	SHIRALEE	RIVER TAMAR	8.2
p	PZ771	SILENUS	COVERACK	6.5
p	PZ1196	SILVER DAWN	NEWLYN	17.9
p	FH506	SILVER LANCE	ST IVES	5.6
p	Ex FH324	SILVER QUEEN	CADGWITH	7.16
p	FH324	SILVER QUEEN	CADGWITH	7.46
p	FY570	SILVERY SEA	NEWLYN	9.6
p	SS723	SIR JACK	NEWLYN	4.8
p	FY120	SIRENE	LOOE	6.5
p	FH443	SOLITAIRE	FALMOUTH	6.49
p	Ex MN199	SOLSTICE	MEVAGISSEY	9.9
p	FH494	SON-A-MOR	COVERACK	6.16
p	PZ5	SOU'WESTER	NEWLYN	5.48
p	FH71	SOUTHERN STAR	COVERACK	4.74
p	FY125	SOUTHERN STAR	SCILLY	9.73
p	FH25	SOVEREIGN	MEVAGISSEY	8.02
p	Ex PZ14	SOWENNA	NEWLYN	18
p	SC181	SOWENNA	NEWLYN	7.85
p	PW3	SPARKLING LINE (Ex GY364)	NEWLYN	17.3
p	Ex P286	SPILGARN	PORTREATH	4.5
p	PW485	SPINDRIFT	PADSTOW	5.64
p	PH307	SPLENDOUR	RIVER TAMAR	7.5
p	PZ218	SPRIGS OF HEATHER	NEWLYN	5.58
p	PZ318	SPRING TIDE	HAYLE	5.67

p	H22	SPURN LIGHT (Ex M21)	LOOE	6
p	PZ64	ST ELVAN	PORTHLEVEN	4.8
p	PZ1053	ST GEORGES	NEWLYN	34.8
p	FH243	ST RUAN	PORTHLEVEN	9.9
p	SC14	STAR of the North (Ex UL4)	NEWLYN	8.49
p	Ex PZ68	STARFISH	PORTHLEVEN	9.6
p	FH414	STARLIGHT	CADGWITH	7.62
p	PH97	STELLA MARIS	RIVER TAMAR	11.3
p	PZ498	STELLISA	NEWLYN	20.6
p	PZ12	STEREN MOR	NEWLYN	7.52
p	SC73	STEREN-MOR	MEVAGISSEY	6.71
p	FH728	STERENNYK	HELFORD RIVER	9.95
p	PZ428	STERGAN	HAYLE	8
p	SS209	STILL WATERS	ST IVES	6.3
p	FH52	STILL WATERS (Ex B522)	MEVAGISSEY	9.87
p	Ex PZ594	STORM PETREL	MEVAGISSEY	4.47
p	Ex PH24	SU JEAN	PADSTOW	9.75
p	FH1	SULA	COVERACK	6.1
p	PH25	SULA BASSANA	RIVER TAMAR	8.2
	SC5	SUMMERTIME BLUES	NEWLYN	6.8
p	FH222	SUNDOWNER	NEWQUAY	9.3
	PZ253	SUNRISE	PENBERTH	4.4
	FH699	SUNSHINE	COVERACK	3.66
	FY826	SUNSHINE	MEVAGISSEY	6.4
p	Ex M65	SUNSTAR	SCILLY	8.53
p	FY509	SUPERB II	MEVAGISSEY	8.53
p	Ex PH583	SURFHUNTER	NEWQUAY	7.15
p	FY759	SURPRISE	MEVAGISSEY	6.72
p	PZ454	SUZIE	ST IVES	4.9
p	FY59	SWALLOW	LOOE	11.7
p	SC46	SWAN DANCER	SCILLY	9.75
p	SS13	SWEET AS	NEWQUAY	5.95
p	FH735	SWEET TART	PORTHLEVEN	5.16
p	H145	SWIFT	HAYLE	9.99
p	Ex WH454	T.K.	BUDE	6.2
p	PZ280	TALISMAN	HELFORD RIVER	9.33
p	Ex PW107	TALLULA	NEWQUAY	9.3
p	FH484	TALLULA	LOOE	7.62
p	FY892	TAMAHINE	LOOE	4.8
p	Ex FH340	TAMALIN	PORTHOUSTOCK	5.03

ALPHABETICAL INDEX by NAME

	Reg	Name		Length	Port
p	FY332	TAMARA		8.5	MEVAGISSEY
p	PZ564	TAMARA		4.5	SENNEN COVE
p	PZ315	TAMSIN T		5.51	NEWLYN
p	FY778	TANEGAN	(Ex LA778)	6.4	LOOE
p	PZ294	TARA ROSE		4.29	MOUSEHOLE
p	SS88	TEGEN MOR		10.8	HAYLE
p	Ex FY863	TEMERAIRE		9.83	LOOE
p	PW214	THOMAS ANDREW		9.83	PADSTOW
p	FH339	THREE BOYS		5.5	MEVAGISSEY
p	PZ718	THREE BOYS		5.04	NEWLYN
p	FY1	THREE JAYS		4.8	GORRAN HAVEN
p	E507	THREE JAYS		7.6	BOSCASTLE
p	FH731	TIDOS		5.55	THE LIZARD
p	SS21	TIGER		5.6	NEWLYN
p	PW433	TIGGER		6.9	PORT ISAAC
p	SS76	TILLERMAN		5.85	NEWLYN
p	Ex PW15	TIME BANDIT		5.92	PADSTOW
p	FY884	TIMMY HAM		4.01	CHARLESTOWN
p	PW16	TIZZARDLEE-ON		9.3	NEWQUAY
p	SS40	TOLLBAR		5.8	NEWQUAY
p	Ex MN203	TONKA		5.88	MEVAGISSEY
p	FY11	TORRI GWYNT	(Ex M11)	4.8	NEWLYN
p	SC1	TORRIBEE	(Ex FH610)	5.85	NEWLYN
p	SS67	TRACEY CLARE		9.94	HELFORD RIVER
p	BN447	TRADITION		6.14	LOOE
p	BF7	TRANQUILITY		20.6	NEWLYN
p	PZ23	TREEN		4.86	NEWLYN
p	FH49	TREGLOWN	(Ex PZ49)	7.87	NEWLYN
p	FH395	TRENEGLOS		8.05	FALMOUTH
p	PZ1228	TRENOW GIRL		4.5	NEWLYN
p	FH2	TREVALLY		7.65	FALMOUTH
p	PZ193	TREVESSA 1V		26.2	NEWLYN
p	FY776	TREWARTHA		6	PADSTOW
p	PZ70	TRISTY		5.85	NEWLYN
p	Ex TH148	TRITON		7.5	NEWLYN
p	FY108	TRUST	(Ex PD108)	7.4	MEVAGISSEY
p	SS233	TRYPHENA		5.6	NEWQUAY
p	SS258	TUDOR ROSE		5.5	PORTHLEVEN
p	PZ826	TUPPENCE		5.54	NEWLYN
p	PZ2499	TWILIGHT		8.02	NEWLYN

	Reg	Name		Length	Port
p	Ex PE585	TWILIGHT		5	RIVER TAMAR
p	PW43	TWILIGHT	(Ex CK3)	5.7	BUDE
p	PZ137	TWILIGHT III		29.1	NEWLYN
p	Ex PZ1212	TWO BOYS		9.99	NEWLYN
p	FY850	TYPHOON		9.9	LOOE
p	Ex PH5595	UNCLE LEN		9	RIVER TAMAR
p	Ex PZ888	UTSKER		9.95	NEWLYN
p	BH9	VALHALLA		10.7	MEVAGISSEY
p	PZ166	VENTURE		5.49	NEWLYN
p	FY58	VENUS		9.95	MEVAGISSEY
p	FY803	VERONA (Ex Wave II)		5.4	MEVAGISSEY
p	FY606	VESPER II	(Ex FY30 & M606)	6.5	MEVAGISSEY
p	FY529	VESTA		7.1	PADSTOW
p	SC32	VICKY ANNA		9.78	SCILLY
p	CK923	VICTORIA		9.9	LOOE
p	FH706	VICTORIA ANN		5.9	CADGWITH
p	SC11	VICTORY of HELFORD		10.7	SCILLY
p	PW473	VIDDY		4.91	LOOE
p	BA284	VIKING		9.84	PADSTOW
p	PZ88	VIKING (Charters)		9.62	PENZANCE
p	Ex PZ481	VIPA		5.6	NEWLYN
p	PZ481	VIPA		6.3	NEWLYN
p	Ex SS12	WAVE DANCER		4.85	HAYLE
p	Ex PZ3	WE-RE HERE		3.17	ST IVES
p	PZ272	WHITE HEATHER		5.6	ST IVES
p	SS33	WHITE HEATHER	(Ex LK3390)	12.4	NEWLYN
p	Ex PZ225	WHITE ROSE		4.6	PORTHGWARRA
p	PZ75	WILLIAM HARVEY		12.6	NEWLYN
p	PZ191	WILLIAM S STEVENSON		28.2	NEWLYN
p	PZ195	WILLIAM STEVENSON		26	NEWLYN
p	SS247	WINKLE		4.42	ST AGNES
p	PZ97	WORTHY LASS		6.15	NEWLYN
p	SS270	ZARA		6.2	MEVAGISSEY
p	PW122	ZARVAN		8.1	NEWQUAY
p	Ex PD1034	ZEPHRON	(Ex FH712)	5	PORTLOE
p	SC50	ZEPHYR		5.84	NEWLYN